CREATE!

Textiles Technology

Julie Messenger
Helen Wilson

Series editor
Jenny Jupe

nn

Inspiring generations

Heinemann Educational Publishers
Halley Court, Jordan Hill, Oxford OX2 8EJ

Part of Harcourt Education

Heinemann is the registered trademark of

Harcourt Education Limited

© Julie Messenger, Helen Wilson, 2003

First published 2003

08 07 06 05 04 03

10 9 8 7 6 5 4 3 2 1

British Library Cataloguing in Publication

Data is available from the British Library on request.

ISBN 0 435 41260 4

Designed, produced and illustrated by Hardlines Ltd,
Charlbury, Oxford

Original illustrations © Harcourt Education Limited,
2003

Cover design by Matt Buckley

Printed in Italy by Printer Trento S.r.l.

Acknowledgements

The publishers would like to thank the following for
permission to reproduce copyright material: The
British Heart Foundation, registered charity, number
225971, p. 40; J.B. Broadley (Permatex 2K), p. 62;
Cooper and Roe, p. 72; Cotton Council International,
p. 33; Kidski, pp. 26-7; Teresa Searle, pp. 24-5;
®Sympatex, the registered trade mark of Sympatex
Technologies GmbH, p. 62; Woolmark, p. 40, the
Woolmark symbol is a registered trademark of the
Woolmark Company.

The publishers would like to thank the following for
permission to reproduce photographs: Action Plus, p.
23 (bottom); Adidas, p. 35 (left); Alamy, p. 79 (left);
Andrew Skelton, p. 25; Bernina Sewing Machines, p.6
(bottom); Bogod & Company Ltd, p. 84 (right);
Brother, pp. 54 (both), 56; Corbis, pp. 22 (centre
bottom, top right), 23 (centre left), 52, 75, 79 (right), 83
(bottom); Deep Light Productions/SPL, p. 72 (right);
Empics, pp. 35 (right), p. 63; FIRA, pp. 65 (bottom),
68; Getty, pp. 23 (top), 64; GS UK Ltd/Brother, p. 85;
Haddon Davies, pp. 11 (top left), 20 (left and right), 28
(left), 29, 31, 33, 42, 44, 45, 46 (right), 53 (bottom), 59,
66, 72 (left); Imagestate/Alamy, p. 53 (top); James King-
Holmes/SPL, pp. 11 (right), 83 (top); Kidski, pp. 26,
27; Photodisc, pp. 46 (left), 60; PhotoObjects, p. 22
(left, centre top, bottom right); Plain Picture/Alamy,
p. 23 (centre right); Popperphoto/Alamy, p. 62 (top);
Singer Sewing Machines, p. 6 (top); Softswitch, p. 61
(right); Stock Connection Inc./Alamy, pp. 76, 91;
Techsoft UK/Roland Stikka, p. 55; Teresa Searle, p. 24;
www.bedexpert.co.uk, p. 61 (left); www.speedstep.de,
p. 82 (left).

Every effort has been made to contact copyright holders
of material reproduced in this book. Any omissions will
be rectified in subsequent printings if notice is given to
the publishers.

There are links to relevant websites in this book. In
order to ensure that the links are up-to-date, that the
links work and that the sites are not inadvertently
linked to sites that could be considered offensive, we
have made the links available on the Heinemann
website at www.heinemann.co.uk/hotlinks. When you
access the site, the express code for this book is 2604P.

Key Stage 3 Strategy links

The following logos are used throughout this book to
highlight different Key Stage 3 Strategy links.

(DMA)	Design and Make Assignment
(D)	Designing
(FPT)	Focused Practical Task
(ICT)	ICT
(ABC)	Literacy
(123)	Numeracy
(PA)	Product analysis
(TS)	Thinking skills

Tel: 01865 888058 www.heinemann.co.uk

Contents

Welcome to Key Stage 3!

Objectives

In this lesson you will:

- find out about Textiles Technology at Key Stage 3
- learn about the different tools and equipment you will be using in Textiles Technology.

Key words

materials	the items different products are made with
equipment	the tools used to make the materials into products

Year 7 means the start of a new school and a new Key Stage. There are many different things about starting a new school: friends, teachers, uniform, is bigger building and, of course, being the youngest class in the school!

Key Stage 3 Design and Technology

Is Key Stage 3 Design and Technology different? Yes and no! You will still be designing and making products that people need, but with different teachers who will help you to learn new skills using some new **materials** and **equipment**.

At Key Stage 3, Design and Technology is taught in a number of specialist rooms, workshops or areas. This means that all the tools and equipment that are needed for each different type of material are kept

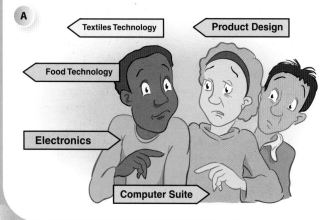

A

Textiles Technology   Product Design

Food Technology

Electronics

Computer Suite

together. Although there are different specialist material work areas and different teachers, they all work together as a team.

Think about it!

1 **TS** Think of a product you made at Key Stage 2. Talk about how you carried out the different activities shown on diagram **B** when designing and making this product.

2 **ABC** In pairs, groups or as a class, discuss the different products you made using textile materials during Key Stage 2.

3 **ABC** Draw a picture and write about a product you made in Key Stage 2 using textile materials.

 a) Who did you make the product for?

 b) What tools and equipment did you use to make the product?

 c) What did you like most about the product you made?

In Design and Technology you will learn things by carrying out focused practical tasks (FPTs), designed to teach you new skills. In Textiles Technology this could be:

- how to use new equipment such as a CNC sewing machine
- how to use specialist computer programs to help you design and make products
- how to carry out different processes: for example to add colour to fabric or to construct different textile products.

You will also carry out product analysis tasks. These involve examining different products in detail to learn:

- who they are designed for
- how they work
- what they are made from
- how they have been designed
- how they have been made.

Focused practical tasks and product analysis tasks help you to build up your knowledge and skills and will help you demonstrate your design and technology capability when you carry out design and make assignments.

B

There are many different activities involved in working through a Design and Make Assignment as you can see in diagram **B**.

The focused practical tasks, product analysis tasks, and design and make assignments you carry out in all the different material areas are linked together, so

that things you learn in one project will help you in other projects.

Key Stage 3 Textiles Technology

This book is all about one of the materials you will be working with during Key Stage 3 – textile materials such as fabric, threads, dyes and inks. Because you may have come from different primary schools, you have probably had different experiences working with textile materials and making different textile products.

There are many different tools and equipment in the Textiles Technology room. Look at picture **C**. It shows some of the different things you will use during Key Stage 3.

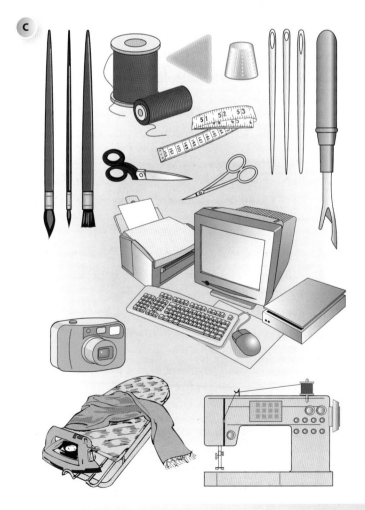

C

Think about it!

1 **TS** Look at the illustrations of textile tools and equipment shown in **C**.

a) Which tools and equipment do you recognize?

b) Which ones have you used before?

c) What did you use them for?

d) Which ones will you need to learn how to use?

2 **ABC** Produce a table showing:

- which tools and equipment you have used before
- what you used them for
- how well you used them
- how easy or difficult they were to use.

3 **ABC** Produce a list of 'dos' and 'do nots' on how to use textiles tools and equipment safely.

Plenary

Key Stage 3 will be different from your experience at Key Stage 2. Your teachers will give you opportunities to build on what you already know and can do as well as giving you the chance to develop new skills. Textiles Technology is just one of several material areas you will be working in during Key Stage 3 Design and Technology. By the time you reach the end of Key Stage 3 you will be a little older and hopefully much wiser!

Tools of the trade: the sewing machine

Objectives

In this lesson you will:

- find out about different sewing machines and how a sewing machine stitch is made
- understand the names of some of the parts on the sewing machine.

Key words

lockstitch a type of sewing machine stitch formed using two threads

bobbin a spool onto which thread is wound

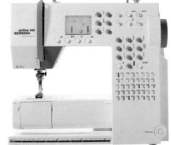

An electric sewing machine is probably one of the most important pieces of equipment you will use in Textiles Technology. In order to design and make good quality textile products, you need to understand how an electric sewing machine works and how to use it properly. In the same way as there are many different cars produced by different car manufacturers, there are also many different sewing machines produced by different sewing machine manufacturers. Some examples are Singer, Brother, Bernina, Elna, Janome, Huskvana-Viking and Pfaff.

Although there are several different makes and models of sewing machine there are two main types: the basic electric and the computerized sewing machines.

Basic electric sewing machines

These machines can be set to produce a range of different stitches. On some machines you have to set the different types of stitches by altering a number of different stitch controls. By altering the different dials or levers, the gears and cams inside the machine are moved so the machine can create different stitches.

Computerized sewing machines

These machines use microchip technology and have a wide range of different stitches that can be selected at the touch of a button. Some computerized sewing machines can produce complicated embroidery designs and can even be linked with computer programs so that you can design your own embroidery designs. You can learn more about this on page 54.

Think about it!

1 **TS** Look at the different sewing machines in your textiles room. As a class, discuss the following questions.

   a) Who are the sewing machines manufactured by?

   b) What is the model name or number of each machine?

   c) What types of sewing machine are they?

2 Do you have a sewing machine at home? What make and model is it?

3 **CT** Produce an information leaflet showing the different models of sewing machine produced by one of the sewing machine manufacturers mentioned at the beginning of this unit. Use the Internet and this website to find out the information you need: www.heinemann.co.uk/hotlinks.

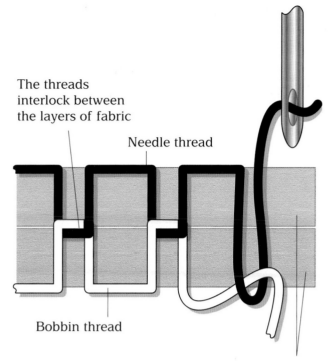

The threads interlock between the layers of fabric

Needle thread

Bobbin thread

Two pieces of fabric

B *How a lockstitch is produced on a sewing machine*

A sewing machine stitch is made in a very different way to sewing by hand. When hand sewing, you have a needle and one length of thread. On a sewing machine there are two threads, one on the top of the machine that goes through the needle, and one underneath the needle that is wound onto a **bobbin**.

Diagram **B** shows how the two threads are twisted together to form a stitch, which is called a **lockstitch**. Visit this website to see an animated sequence showing exactly how a lockstitch is formed: www.heinemann.co.uk/hotlinks

Although there are many different makes and models of domestic sewing machine, the way a sewing machine stitch is formed is the same on all of them. This means that all sewing machines have some things in common.

Diagram **C** shows the different parts typically found on all sewing machines. Compare this diagram with the machines used in school so that you can recognize the different parts and understand what they do.

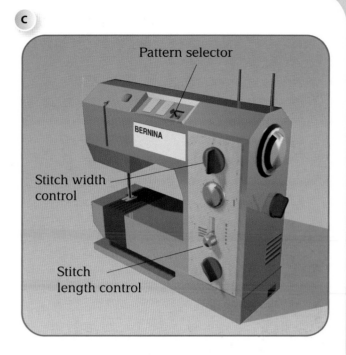

C

Pattern selector

BERNINA

Stitch width control

Stitch length control

(FPT) *Thread the sewing machine*

You will need to be able to thread up the sewing machine for yourself. Follow the instructions and ask your teacher for help if you need to. This skill needs practice so that you can become quick and accurate!

Think about it!

1 (PA) Look at the sewing machine you are using in school, can you find the same parts that are shown on diagram **C**?

2 (ABC) Learn the names of the different parts of a sewing machine. Make sure you know how to spell them and what they do.

3 (ICT) Use the basic shapes in Microsoft Word AutoShapes to produce a sheet of simple line shapes. Practice your sewing skills by stitching over the lines.

Plenary

Sewing machines are 'the same – but different'! When you have learned how to use one sewing machine you will be able to apply this knowledge when you use a different make or model of machine. Just in the same way that when you have learned how to drive you can drive different makes of car!

All stitched up!

Objectives

In this lesson you will find out about different types of stitches that are used when making textile products.

Key words

functional or **utility stitches**   stitches that are used to construct products

Machine stitching

All modern sewing machines can do a variety of different stitches. The type and number of stitches will depend on the model; usually the more expensive the machine the more stitches it will do.

Some stitches are called **functional** or **utility stitches** because they are used for a specific job or function such as sewing seams, neatening edges, sewing on elastic and making buttonholes.

Some sewing machine stitches are decorative. These can be used in many different ways on textile products to make them look more attractive. Sometimes decorative stitches can be functional as well, such as using a decorative stitch to secure a hem in place.

If you are using a computerized sewing machine, you may only need to press a button to make the machine do the different stitches. If you are using a basic electric sewing machine, you will have to set the different stitch controls yourself. Check the instructions to find out how to do this.

FPT Machine stitches

1   Have a look at the sewing machine you are using.

   a) How many different functional stitches will your sewing machine do?

   b) How many decorative stitches will your sewing machine do?

   c) How do you set the sewing machine to make the different stitches?

   d) Produce a stitch sample showing some of the functional stitches that can be done on a sewing machine. Mount your sample and draw a table to show the settings on the stitch controls you used for each stitch.

2   **D** Use three different decorative stitches and two different thread colours to produce a sample of a decorative border design that could be stitched around the bottom of the legs of a pair of denim jeans.

3   **TS** When you are sewing your samples, see if you can work out how the machine is making the different stitches.

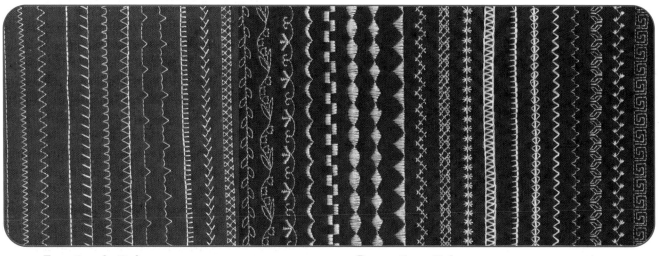

←——Functional stitches ——→   ←———————— Decorative stitches ————————→

A   *Stitches available on a Brother Super Ace III sewing machine*

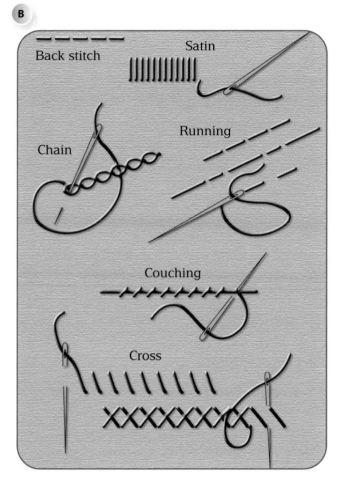

B

Back stitch

Satin

Chain

Running

Couching

Cross

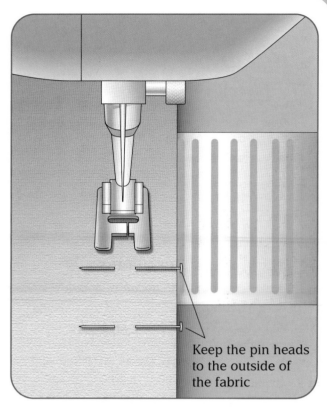

Keep the pin heads to the outside of the fabric

C *If you put your pins at right-angles to the direction you are sewing, and stitch slowly, you can stitch over the pins with the sewing machine.*

Hand stitching

Although you will often use a sewing machine, there will be times when you need to sew by hand, such as:

- when tacking fabric pieces together temporarily
- when finishing off different parts of your product for example, hems
- when adding some types of decoration to your products for example, hand embroidery.

Just a minute!

When you are making textile products you sometimes need to hold the fabric pieces together temporarily, such as:

- when modelling design ideas with fabric
- to check that fabric pieces will fit together
- to hold the fabric pieces together while you are sewing – this is particularly important if the fabrics you are working with are difficult to handle.

In these situations, you could use hand tacking stitches, a long straight sewing machine stitch or pins.

Think about it!

1   **TS** Look at the different stitches shown in **B**. Which stitches do you know how to do?

2   **TS** When have you used hand stitches to make textiles products in Key Stage 2?

FPT Hand stitches

Using a selection of decorative hand stitches, produce a name badge that you could wear during your textiles lessons so that your teacher can learn your name!

Plenary

Stitches can be functional or decorative (or both!), permanent or temporary, produced by hand or by machine. The stitches you choose to use in your practical work will depend on the type of product you are making, the function of the stitching and the manufacturing system that would be used to produce your product.

Getting started !

Objectives

In this lesson you will find out about different types of patterns used in Textiles Technology.

Key words

pattern	a paper shape used as a template for cutting out fabric pieces
pattern drafting	the process of making patterns for textile products
pattern markings	special symbols marked onto pattern pieces
seam allowance	the extra fabric needed to make a seam that is added to a pattern piece

Textile products are made by joining together flat pieces of fabric. It is important to work out the shapes of the fabric pieces accurately before you start to cut out your fabric. Each shape can be drawn on paper to produce a **pattern**. The paper pattern is then pinned onto the fabric so that the fabric pieces can be cut out accurately. Making patterns for textile products is called **pattern drafting**.

Pattern drafting

Drafting patterns for textile products involves an understanding of:
- the flat shapes different products are made from
- the different processes that can be used to put the fabric pieces together.

Some textile products, such as cushions and simple bags, are made from simple shapes that are relatively easy to draft. Other products, such as garments, are more complicated and need much more skill. In industry there are specialist pattern technologists whose job is to draft the patterns for the garments that have been designed.

Pattern markings

Special symbols are marked onto patterns to help you make the product accurately – look at **A**.

Ready-made patterns

When making textile products in school, you can use ready-made patterns as these have been drafted and checked to make sure that they work. There are plenty of different places you can find ready-made patterns – for example, in magazines, specialist

A

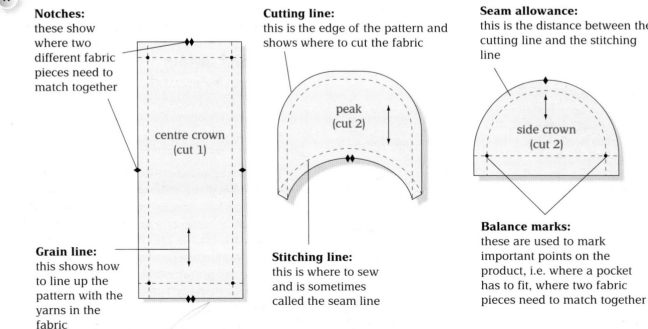

Notches: these show where two different fabric pieces need to match together

Cutting line: this is the edge of the pattern and shows where to cut the fabric

Seam allowance: this is the distance between the cutting line and the stitching line

peak (cut 2)

centre crown (cut 1)

side crown (cut 2)

Grain line: this shows how to line up the pattern with the yarns in the fabric

Stitching line: this is where to sew and is sometimes called the seam line

Balance marks: these are used to mark important points on the product, i.e. where a pocket has to fit, where two fabric pieces need to match together

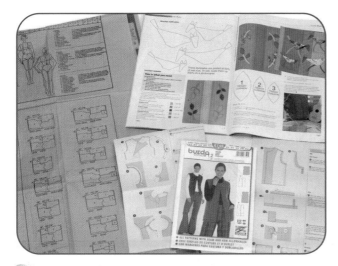

B *A selection of ready-made patterns*

books, on specialist websites on the Internet and from pattern manufacturers (photo **B**).

Some patterns are printed full size so that they are ready to use. Sometimes the patterns are printed onto a grid at a smaller scale, to save paper. These types of pattern will need to be enlarged to make them full size.

Drafting your own patterns

Drafting your own pattern can be done in two ways.

- By hand – drawing out the different pattern shapes using a pencil and ruler on paper. This involves accurate measuring and drawing skills (see **C**).
- Using ICT – for this you need a special pattern-drafting program such as Fittingly Sew (Soft Byte) or Pattern Maker (Pro Specs). Look at photo **D**.

C

D

Think about it!

1   **PA** Look at a commercial pattern and identify the different pattern markings that have been used. Draw one of the pattern pieces and label the different pattern markings.

2   **ICT** **123** Draft a pattern for a cover for your school organizer using a pattern-drafting program.

3   **FPT** Manufacture your organizer cover and check that it will fit!

DMA *Glove puppet*

A local playgroup has asked you to make a glove puppet that could be used during story-time sessions with the children. Design and make a puppet based on a character from a popular children's book or story.

Plenary

Do not get confused – the word 'pattern' can mean two different things in Textiles Technology! In this unit it is used to describe the paper shapes used to cut out fabric pieces. A pattern can also refer to the design on a piece of fabric! Whatever textile product you are going to make, you need to start with an accurate pattern. Build up your skills by using ready-made patterns and drafting your own simple patterns.

Looking at fibres and fabrics

Objectives

In this lesson you will:
- find out what fabrics are
- learn how fabrics are made.

Key words

fibre	the smallest part of a fabric
staple fibre	a short fibre
continuous filament fibre	a very long fibre

Close your eyes for a minute and imagine a life without any textile products. Think about sleeping without any bedding or having a bath without a towel, living without any clothing or travelling in a car with out seats or tyres! Would life be easy?

Where do fabrics come from?

Fabrics are manufactured from a **yarn**, which is made from **fibres**. A fibre is the smallest element of a fabric; it looks rather like a human hair. Fibres come from several different sources; they can be either natural or manufactured. Natural fibres come from animals or plants.

Manufactured fibres come from two different sources. They can be made from minerals such as oil or coal, or they are natural fibres which have chemicals added to them. These fibres are referred to as regenerated cellulose fibres. For example, rayon, wood pulp or cotton waste (cellulose) are mixed with chemicals to manufacture regenerated fibres.

How are fabrics made?

Before a fabric can be manufactured, a yarn has to be produced. Yarns are made from fibres. Each fibre has its own set of properties, and each method of making a fabric has its own set of characteristics. The fibre and a method of making a fabric combine together to produce fabrics that are suitable for very different uses. There are three main methods used to manufacture fabrics:
- weaving
- knitting
- bonding.

Natural fibres are usually short and known as **staple fibres**. Manufactured fibres are very long and are known as **continuous filament fibres**. **Micro-fibres** are fibres that are manufactured so they are ten times finer than a human hair. These fine fibres are used to make modern fabrics, often from a manufactured source, such as Tencel.

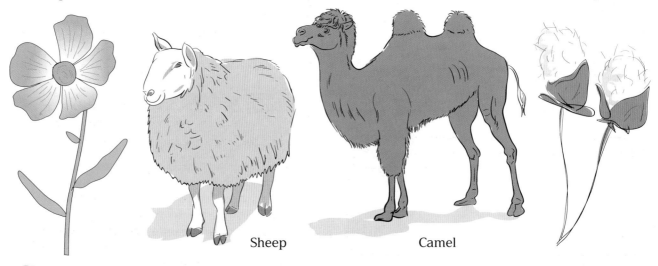

Flax plant · Sheep · Camel · Cotton plant

A *Natural fibres come from animals or plants*

Weaving – a woven fabric is a strong fabric

Woven fabrics are made from weaving two yarns together, using a loom. The yarn that is used from the top to the bottom of the loom is the warp thread. The yarn that goes under and over the warp yarn is known as the weft thread. Where the weft thread turns around at the edge of a fabric it is known as the selvedge.

B

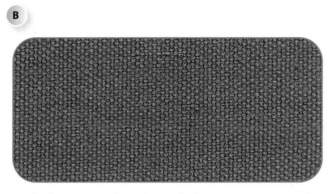

Knitting – a knitted fabric is a stretchy fabric

Knitting is forming loops on a set of needles and pulling a thread through the loops. There are two main methods of knitting.

- Weft knitting is where loops interlock across the width of the fabric.
- Warp knitting can only be produced on a knitting machine. This is where the yarns themselves are interlocked along the length of the fabric and both sides of the fabric look identical.

C

Fabric	Fabric pulled vertically	Fabric pulled horizontally	Fabric pulled diagonally
Woven	Stays firm		
Knitted			
Bonded			

E *Characteristics of fabrics*

Bonding – a bonded fabric is a weak fabric

Fibres are bonded together by heating, gluing or stitching the fibres together. A bonded fabric has no weft or warp threads and no right or wrong side. They are usually inexpensive fabrics that do not fray, such as felt or stitch and tear vilene.

D

Think about it!

1 **TS** Take a piece of yarn and unravel the yarn to examine the fibre.

   a) What does the fibre look like?

   b) How long is the fibre when unravelled from the yarn?

   c) Is the fibre a short staple fibre or a long continuous filament fibre?

   d) Think about your findings. Can you now say what fibre your fabric has been made from? Is it a natural or man-made fibre? Why do you think so?

2 **TS** Take 10cm × 10cm pieces of woven, knitted and bonded fabrics and conduct the following tests.

   a) Pull each fabric sample vertically, horizontally and diagonally. What happens?

   b) Record your findings on a table like the one in **E**.

   c) Why do you think this information is important when you are looking at fabrics?

Plenary

Fabrics can be grouped according to the fibres they are made from or how they are made. To understand why fabrics behave in the way they do, you need to understand what fabrics are made from and how they are made.

Selecting the correct fabric

Objectives

In this lesson you will:

- learn how to select a fabric for the product you are going to manufacture
- conduct simple tests to check how a fabric behaves.

Key words

characteristics the qualities of a fabric

absorbency the ability to soak up moisture

Choosing a fabric for the textile product you want to make can be a very difficult process. In this section you will be designing and manufacturing a safety badge for person under sixteen years of age. The fabrics you choose will need to have very special properties and there are hundreds of fabrics to choose from.

How do you know which fabric will be the best choice?

- Do you look at rolls of fabrics and decide which one is best because of how it looks and feels?
- Do you look closely at the fabric and make a choice because of the way the fabric has been constructed?
- Do you consider which fibres have been used to make the yarn to produce the fabric?

A How do you know which fabric will be best for your product?

The fibres, combined with the way the fabric has been manufactured, will begin to shape up the way the fabric looks and feels and how it will behave. When selecting a fabric, you need to match the looks and the feel of a fabric with the properties or **characteristics** you need for the product you are manufacturing.

Fibre	Durability (wear-ability)	Strength	Flamm-ability	Warmth	Elasticity	Absorbency	Cost
Cotton	★★★★	★★★★	★	★★★	★★★★	★★★★★	medium
Polyester	★★★★★	★★★★★	★★★★★				low
Wool	★★	★	★★★	★★★★★	★★★★★	★★★★	high
Rayon	★	★★★	★			★★★	medium
Nylon (tactel)	★★★★★	★★★★★	★★★★★		★★★★★		low

B Fibre properties table

Key ★★★★★ = good performance ★ = poor performance.

Method of construction	Properties
Woven	Usually a strong fabric
Knitted	Usually a stretchy fabric
Bonded	Usually a weak fabric

C   *Fabric construction methods*

Fabric finishes

Once a fabric has been constructed, it goes through another process to add value to the fabric. This additional process is referred to as the fabric finish. The surface of the fabric is altered to enable it to have additional properties.

Think about it!

1   Look at table **B**.

a) Which fibres are the strongest?

b) Which fibre absorbs moisture the best?

2   **FPT** To be suitable for the safety badge you are manufacturing your fabric needs to have certain properties. Write a list of the properties the fabric needs, and give reasons for these characteristics.

This list is a very simple fabric specification. You will learn more about fabric specifications on pages 16–17.

Finishing processes

Mechanical – a machine alters the surface of the fabric to change its characteristics.

Chemical – chemicals are added to the surface of the fabric to enable it to perform in a specific way.

Coating – a layer of a substance is applied to a base fabric to enable it to have different properties.

Laminating – two or more fabrics are bonded together to create another fabric with improved properties.

D   *Finishes that can be applied to fabrics*

The following questions will help you to draw up a list of the properties your fabric must have to be suitable for the safety badge you are making.

Does the safety badge need to be:

- washed or dry cleaned
- strong or weak
- stiff or floppy
- absorbent or water resistant
- bright or dull
- opaque
- warm
- biodegradable
- flameproof
- quick to dry
- stain resistant
- easily seen
- windproof
- shrink resistant?

Does it need to:

- drape well
- feel soft or rough?

E   FABRIC SPECIFICATION

Plenary

There may well be more than one fabric that could be used to make the safety badge. The hardest part is to identify the characteristics the fabric must have to be an ideal fabric for the badge.

A testing time

Objectives

In this lesson you will:

- learn how to look at fabrics and make decisions about how they behave
- test fabrics to check out how they behave.

Key words

fraying where the yarn comes away from the cut edge easily

shrinkage how much a fabric is reduced in size once it has been wet

How do fabrics behave?

By looking closely at fabrics, perhaps using a magnifying glass, as well as by touching them you can make decisions about how the fabric will behave. Looking and feeling a fabric will help you to decide on whether a fabric is:

- rough or smooth
- warm or cool
- heavy or light weight
- transparent or opaque
- stiff or floppy.

To determine the additional properties of a fabric requires special tests. There are several different simple tests that you can carry out with basic equipment to see how a fabric behaves. The following tests can help you decide on which fabric is the best for the safety badge you are designing.

Testing fabrics

Select three different fabrics that you could use to make the safety badge. You will need two 10 x 10 cm square samples of each fabric you are testing. You will perform tests 1, 2 and 3 on one of the squares and tests 4 and 5 on the other. For each fabric, carry out the following tests.

Test 1: for fraying

Look closely at the fabric and try to pull the fabric apart. How easily does the yarn come away from the

fabric? If the yarn comes away easily then the fabric is said to fray easily. If it doesn't come away easily then the fabric does not fray easily. Generally speaking, fabrics that do not fray easily are fabrics that are easier to work with.

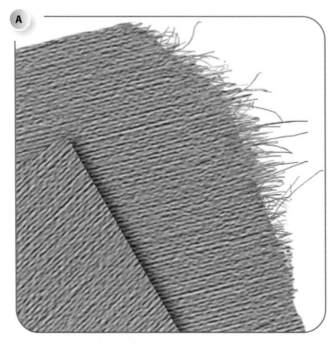

A

Test 2: for stretch

Take a piece of the fabric and pull the opposite edges of the fabric and then let go of one edge. Does the fabric return to it starting size?

B

Test 3: for creasing

Squeeze the fabric in your hand, keep it scrunched up for a few minutes and then let go. See how much the fabric creases. If the fabric has many creases, then the fabric creases easily. If the fabric springs back and has few if any creases, it is said to be **crease resistant**.

C

Test 4: for absorbency

Using a pipette, drop water onto the surface of the fabric sample. If the water soaks into the fabric, the fabric is absorbent. Depending on how much water the fabric will absorb will show how absorbent the fabric is.

D

Test 5: for shrinkage

Accurately measure the fabric before you start, and write down the results. Then handwash the fabric in hand-hot water with a detergent. Rinse and dry the fabric (you could use a hair dryer for this) and then measure it again. Is the fabric smaller than when you started? If so, then the fabric has shrunk.

E

Think about it!

ABC For each of the three fabrics you have tested, write a report outlining what you have discovered during the testing.

1 The report should include a sample of the fabric and written information about the characteristics of the fabric.

2 You need to state whether the fabric is suitable for the safety badge or not. If it is a good choice of fabric, give the reasons why.

3 Give the fabric a suitability rating, which is a mark out of 10. For example, 7 marks out of 10 suggest that it is a reasonably good fabric to make the safety badge from.

Plenary

A textile designer needs to choose the correct fabric for the products they are manufacturing. Basic tests are completed to check that a fabric has some of the obvious properties that are required.

Designing a safety badge

Objectives

In this lesson you will:

- learn that special fabrics provide protection in the dark

- think about what you have to consider before you start designing solutions to the problem you have been presented with.

Key words

fluorescent fabric	a brightly coloured fabric that reflects light rays
reflective fabric	light is reflected from the surface of the fabric

Special fabrics

Many fabrics have been produced to help protect us against hazards in our daily lives. There are some special fabrics that have been developed to be seen in the dark. These fabrics are used in some of the clothing that is suitable for young children such as outdoor clothing, gloves, rucksacks and on the heels of trainers.

A

Visibilty of a pedestrian at night

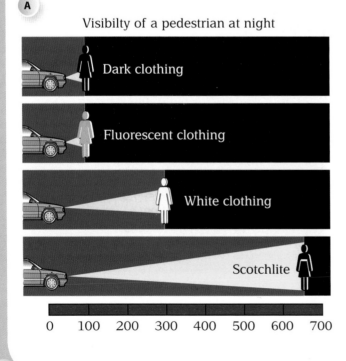

The colour of the fabric makes a difference as to whether it can be seen in the dark. Being seen in the twilight or dark is important to a whole range of people who spend time outdoors, such as:

- emergency service workers
- walkers, hikers, cyclists
- schoolchildren walking home after school
- elderly people.

Both **fluorescent fabrics** and **reflective fabrics** are more easily seen in the dark and help to protect people when they are outside in poor light.

Modern fabrics that can be seen in the dark

Reflective fabrics are made in a number of ways. Some reflective fabrics have mini sataLITE dishes embedded into the fabric (see diagram **B**). These disks ensure light is reflected back to the source, which makes the fabric very visible. Another type of reflective fabric, Sun Lite, is created by glass spheres being bonded with a special glue to a base fabric. Both of these methods produce strips and sheets of reflective material. IllumiNITE is the trade name of a reflective material where the complete fabric is coated in a reflective dye that is only visible at night. IllumiNITE allows the whole silhouette of a person to be seen at night rather than just a strip.

B

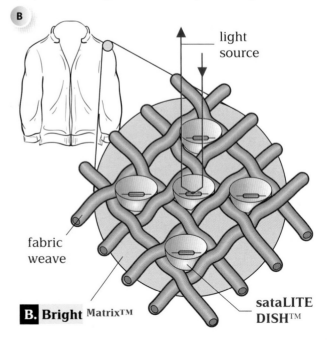

Designing a safety badge

The most effective fabrics for us to use are those that can be seen in the dark. We must consider using light-coloured fabrics, fluorescent fabrics and reflective fabrics when designing the safety badge.

You also need to think carefully about several issues.

- Who will be using the badge?
- Why do they need a safety badge?
- What is the function of the badge?
- Where will the badge be positioned?
- How will the badge be attached to the user?
- What fabrics are available to design the badge with?
- Does the badge have to be a certain size?
- What is already available to protect people from the dark?

You should now be in a position to start sketching some initial design ideas.

Think about it!

1 Draw a thought bubble to present your answers to the questions listed on this page.

2 Are there any other questions you need to find out answers to?

Plenary

There are special fabrics available to textile designers. You must know what fabrics and materials are available to you before you start designing a product. You need to constantly be on the look out for new and modern materials with very definite properties for specific functions. Ensure you have all the information you need to design a solution that will answer the problem. Check this out first and have a clear direction to your design brief. This will avoid wasting time when designing.

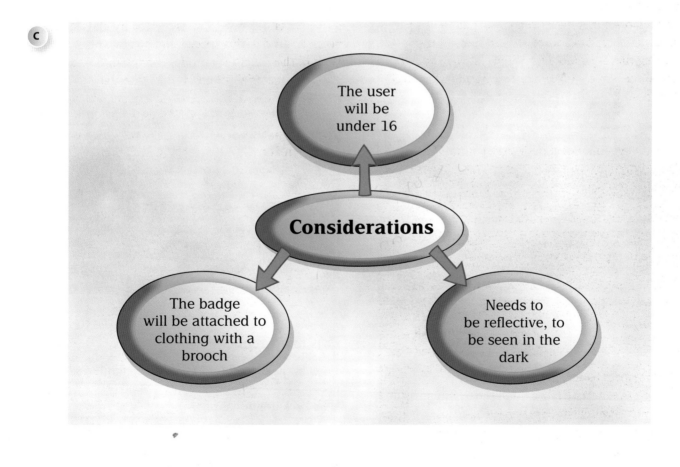

c

The user will be under 16

Considerations

The badge will be attached to clothing with a brooch

Needs to be reflective, to be seen in the dark

Adding colour to a fabric

Objectives

In this lesson you will learn how to appliqué fabrics to decorate your safety badge.

Key words

appliqué — the decorative process of attaching one fabric to another using stitches

Colour can be added to a fabric either by adding other fabrics, threads or **components,** or by using dyes and paints. There are reflective fabrics available as well as dyes that have phosphorous added to them to enable them to shine in the dark.

A

For the safety badge, it would probably be a good idea to use reflective fabrics and the technique called **appliqué**. Appliqué uses satin stitch (a close together zig-zag stitch) to attach one or more fabrics to a background fabric. This is one way you could attach reflective tapes and other florescent fabrics to make a safety badge.

Factfile

- Appliqué is used when one fabric is stitched onto another fabric to add interest to the final product.
- Appliqué can be used on most textile products.
- It is often used on products for young children.
- Appliqué is usually worked before the pieces of fabric are stitched together to make a product.
- Machine appliqué is an effective and fairly easy process, but it relies on good machine skills to ensure that the quality of the finished product is high.
- The best results are produced when the appliqué shapes are clear, simple and of a reasonable size. This means that it is easier to machine around the shapes to get a good finish.

B   *Examples of appliqué*

How to do appliqué

Look at the diagrams in **C**. To do appliqué you will need:

- a background fabric
- a fabric to appliqué
- Bondaweb (a fabric that will stick your appliqué shapes temporarily on the background fabric while you machine them in place permanently).

c

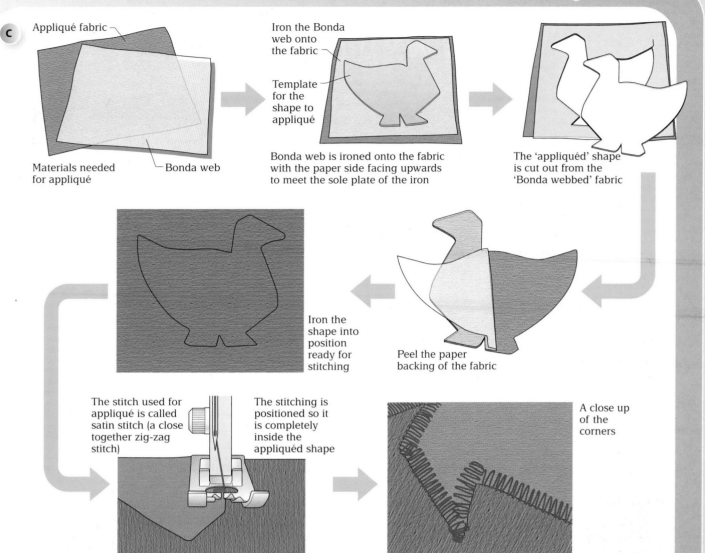

Appliqué fabric

Materials needed for appliqué

Bonda web

Iron the Bonda web onto the fabric

Template for the shape to appliqué

Bonda web is ironed onto the fabric with the paper side facing upwards to meet the sole plate of the iron

The 'appliquéd' shape is cut out from the 'Bonda webbed' fabric

Iron the shape into position ready for stitching

Peel the paper backing of the fabric

The stitch used for appliqué is called satin stitch (a close together zig-zag stitch)

The stitching is positioned so it is completely inside the appliquéd shape

A close up of the corners

🅕🅟🅣 Appliqué

Take three pieces of background fabric (a firm woven fabric such as calico would be ideal). Using another firm woven fabric in a contrasting colour with Bondaweb attached to the wrong side of it, cut out three different shapes using the suggestions below.

- Use straight lines only to create a random abstract shape.
- Use curved and straight lines to create an abstract shape.
- Use curved lines only to create an abstract shape.

Peel the paper backing from the Bondaweb shapes and iron them into position on the background fabric. Machine around each abstract shape to fix it permanently onto the background fabric.

Think about it!

🆃🆂 Talk to your teacher about the samples of appliqué you have produced.

1   Which shapes did you find the easiest to machine around? Why was this so?

2   What kind of shape would be good to use on your safety badge? Why?

Plenary

Appliqué is a simple way of adding colour to a fabric. It looks very professional when the stitches are correctly positioned, and the shapes attached are simple and clear to see. If the shapes are too small, the technique is very difficult to do and messy to look at. The tip here is to keep shapes bold and with few very tightly curved lines. Straight lines and very slight curves work best.

Whose hat?

Objectives

In this lesson you will:

- think about customers' needs and wants
- find out about the things designers have to consider when designing products.

Key words

target customer the person or group of people a product is designed for

Customers buy a product because they need it or want it. Hats are needed by different people for all sorts of different reasons (see photo **A**).

Design decisions

There are many things a designer needs to think about when designing a new product.

- The **target customer**: Who is the product for? How old are they? What sex are they?
- The function of the product: What has the product got to do? How and when will the customer use the product?
- The size of the product: What size does the product need to be?
- The cost of the product: How much will it cost to make and sell the product? Will the target customer buy it? Will the company make a profit?
- The fabric the product will be made from: Is the fabric right for the function of the product? Will the fabric appeal to the customer?
- The number of products to make: How many customers are likely to buy the product? Will it be a one-off product? Will hundreds, thousands or even more identical products be made?
- How the product will be made: What machines and processes will be used to join the fabric pieces together?
- How the product will be sold: How will the customers find out that the product is available to buy?
- Where the product will be sold: Will the customers be able to buy the product easily? What different places could the customer buy the product from?
- The life of the product: How long does the product need to last? What will happen to the product when it is no longer needed?

A

Designers have to think about the needs and wants of customers when they are designing new products. For example, cycle helmets are needed for protection but different cyclists want different types of helmets. A racing cyclist will want an aerodynamically-shaped helmet while a child will want a helmet that is colourful and fun to wear. Designers also have to think about the function of products. As we lose a lot of heat from our heads, it is very important to keep your head warm when you are out on a cold day or when you are taking part in outdoor winter activities like skiing and snowboarding.

B

Think about it!

1 **PA** **TS** Look at the pictures of different types of hats in **A**.

a) Who would wear each hat?

b) When would each hat be worn?

c) Why would each hat be worn?

d) Produce a table to record your answers.

e) What other reasons can you think of for wearing hats?

2 **TS** **ABC** Collect some examples of other of types of hats. Explain who would wear them and why.

3 **TS** Look at the different winter hats in **B**.

a) Who have they been designed for?

b) How has the designer considered the needs and wants of the customer?

4 **PA** **TS** **ABC** Produce a table to record the answers to these questions

a) What types of hat do you have?

b) When do you wear them?

c) Why do you wear them?

d) Why did you choose the particular styles you did?

5 **TS** **ABC** You can find out a lot more about a product if you are able to handle it. Find a winter hat of your own or from a member of your family. Evaluate the hat carefully and explain:

a) who the hat is worn by

b) when and why it is worn

c) why the hat was chosen

d) what fabric it is made from

e) where it was made

f) how it should be cared for.

Plenary

Designers have to make things that people need and will want to buy. Remember this when you are designing the products you make in your Design and Technology lessons.

An interview with Teresa Searle

When did you start to design and make hats for sale?

I began making hats at college in 1985 when I was studying textile design. After leaving I set up a business and began to sell them to make a living.

Who do you design and make your hats for?

My main age range is 35-65. I have recently started a new range which is aimed at younger people, aged 18 plus. Sometimes I make baby and child hats but they are very expensive for children's clothing and I tend to make them mainly for friends and relatives.

What different styles of hats do you produce?

At the moment I only produce two styles of hat. I used to make about seven styles but decided to cut down and concentrate more on pattern and colour.

How do you decide what style of hat to design and make?

I look at many shapes of hats in magazines, in shops, and traditional hats from other cultures. I try on hats in shops. I also make 'toile' hats and try them on to see what works. I want styles that are not over-fussy, as the main interest is the pattern and colour.

How many of each style do you make? Are they all the same?

I repeat the styles of hats for many years, changing the patterns and colours all the time so they look very different from each other.

How long does it take to make one hat?

The simpler hats may only take one hour, the more complicated ones may take up to five hours. I rarely make just one hat; I normally make them in batches of up to twenty. It is quicker to work this way as I can cut them all out at the same time, sew them all up at the same time, press them all at the same time and so on.

What type of fabrics are your hats made from?

I use a special fabric called felted knitting. I have Shetland wool and lambswool yarn knitted up on a knitting machine in lengths. I then put the lengths into the washing machine on a long, hot wash (the Shetland wool is washed at 60°C and the lambswool at 30°C). The washing machine provides heat moisture and friction which makes the fibres matt together, shrink and felt up.

Why have you chosen this/these fabrics?

My college tutor suggested that I try felting knitting and I loved it immediately. The fabric is soft and warm and ideal for winter hats and other accessories. It can be cut without running or fraying and it is ideal for appliqué.

How are your hats decorated?

I use appliqué. The hat is cut out of felt, then other felt shapes are sewn on using zig zag sewing machine stitch to form a design.

B

How do you advertise and sell your hats?

The main way that I sell my hats is through craft and applied art galleries or designer clothing shops. Some of them buy work directly from me. Others will take work on 'sale or return' which means that I do not get any money until they have sold the work. The best way to let shops and galleries know about your work is to take a stand at a trade fair where many gallery and shop owners walk round and look at new work. I have taken part in trade shows in Britain, San Francisco and New York.

Another way that I sell work is through exhibitions. A gallery will make a special display of work for a short time and publicise it in magazines etc. Sometimes I take part in craft fairs and sell direct to the public. This has the advantage of meeting customers and seeing what they like and what suits people. Another way of making work known to people is to have a magazine article or feature on television or radio programmes.

FPT Felted fabrics

Try making your own knitted felted fabrics using old woollen jumpers and washing them at a high temperature in a washing machine. Then use the fabric to make a simple textiles product.

How do you get ideas for the decoration?

I have a sketchbook where I draw ideas from life or from books or postcards. I also stick in magazine cuttings, and photos, swatches and samples. I use the information I have collected to inspire and inform me

Teresa ♥ Searle

FELTED KNITWEAR WITH APPLIQUE

in my design work. One of the richest sources of design comes from gardens such as my own small garden and even very large ornamental gardens such as the Alhambra, in Granada, Spain. Flowers, leaves, trees and birds feature in my work frequently. I also love mosaics, folk art from all cultures but especially from America and Eastern Europe, and modern and contemporary art such as Matisse, Klimt and Andy Goldsworthy.

How much do your hats cost to buy?

They range from £49 for the simple styles to £89 for the more complicated ones.

Think about it!

ICT Find out more about the different products Teresa Searle designs and makes using felted fabrics by visiting this website: www.heinemann.co.uk/hotlinks.

Use this information to produce an A4 poster that could be used to advertise an exhibition of her work at an art gallery.

Plenary

Craft-produced products are made as one-off items or in small quantities. They often include hand processes and are made by one person. The design of the product can be made to suit the specific requirements of an individual customer.

An interview with Kidski

Objectives

In this lesson you will:

- find out about **industrial production**
- learn about the factors that influence the design and manufacture of hats that are made in large quantities.

Key words

industrial production	large quantities of identical products produced for a target customer group

When was Kidski started?

My wife and I started Kidski in 1999.

Why did you decide to set up your company?

Linda (my wife) was standing waiting for the kids to come out of school one springtime and heard some of the other parents saying how they could not get any affordable ski clothes for their kids now that C&A no longer had outlets in the UK. We recognized a gap in the market and decided to do some research.

Who are Kidski products designed for?

Our products are aimed at children but also at the parents who are the ones who actually buy the goods.

What different styles of hats do you supply?

We supply different ranges of hats from the very practical and functional such as the trapper hat and the wool hats, to the more fun and functional such as the Adley Hat and the cow and rabbit balaclavas.

How do you decide what styles of hats to include in your range?

We try and get something for everyone so that parents will buy them because they are 'sensible' and the kids will want to wear them because they are either fun or 'cool' to wear.

How many of each style do you stock?

This is down to supply and demand. Because we have only been running a few years, we are still building up a customer profile but we have already established that the more functional hats are going better than the fun ones – probably because of the person who is actually paying for them!

Where/how are your hats manufactured?

Our hats are currently manufactured in France using the latest technology, though we are looking at other suppliers worldwide all the time.

What type of fabrics are your hats made from?

The hats we choose are predominantly of fleece and wool.

Why have you chosen these fabrics?

These materials are used for two main reasons, warmth and comfort. Materials used today have improved immensely over the years and now provide the wearers the very best protection whilst out on the slopes. Because the materials stretch they fit pretty much any head.

How much do your hats cost?

Between £9.00 and £12.00.

How do you advertise and sell Kidski products?

Our products are advertised and sold predominantly over the Internet using our own shopping basket and secure website. We also sell by mail order and this has increased a lot over the last year. We find a lot of people like to receive one of our catologues so they can have a look at the garments first, they then either buy online or phone their order through.

Think about it!

1 **ICT** Find out more about the products manufactured by Kidski by using the following website : www.heinemann.co.uk/hotlinks. Use this information to produce an advertisement that could be included in a winter sports magazine.

2 **FPT** Produce a table to compare the differences between the hats designed and produced by Kidski and by Teresa Searle.

3 **ABC** Find out about the styles of ski hats that can be bought in shops near where you live or from catalogues. Produce a picture sheet showing different styles that might appeal to the young teenage market. Explain why the styles you have selected would be suitable for this target customer group.

Plenary

Industrially-produced hats are manufactured in large quantities by a workforce. The design of the products has to appeal to a large group of people (the target market). There is little if any handwork done when making large quantities of the same product as this would increase the cost of the product.

B

Have fun with fleece

Objectives

In this lesson you will:

- find out about fleece fabrics
- understand how to join fleece fabric together.

Key words

working characteristics	how a fabric behaves when it is being manufactured into products
seam	a join to hold two or more pieces of fabric together

All about fleece fabrics

Winter hats need to keep you warm so they need to be made from fabrics that have good insulation properties. Place a piece of fleece fabric over the back of your hand and it will soon start to feel warm. This is because the heat from your hand warms up the air that is between the fibres and yarns inside the fleece fabric. Fleece fabric is a knitted fabric that has been brushed to make the surface fluffy. This is called the **pile**.

A   *Printed and plain fleece fabrics, available from Pennine Outdoor*

FPT Investigating fleece

1. Look at the labels inside a number of different fleece garments to find out what fibres they have been made from. What are the most commonly used fibres?
2. Some fleece fabrics have a brand name, for example Polartec®. What other brand names can you find?
3. Collect some examples of different fleece fabrics.

B

POLARTEC®

Polartec® is a registered trademark of Malden Mills Industries, Lawrence, MA

Think about it!

1. ABC Collect some advertisements for different garments made from branded fleece fabric. Discuss how the advertisement has been presented to appeal to the target customer.
2. ICT Find out more about fleece fabrics by searching the Internet. Type 'fleece fabrics' into a search engine.
3. Use the information you have found out in these activities to produce a class display about fleece fabrics and garments.

Working with fleece fabrics

Before you start to design and make a product it is important to understand about the **working characteristics** of the fabric you are using. This will help you decide:

- what style of product would be suitable with a certain fabric
- what processes to use when you join the fabric pieces together and finish off the edges.

Fleece fabric is stretchy because it is a knitted fabric (remember what you learned in Unit 2). Different types of fleece fabric have different amounts of stretch; different parts of your product may need to be stretched more than other parts. It is important that you choose a sewing machine stitch that will stretch where the hat needs to stretch.

FPT Sewing seam samples

Try out three **seam** samples. Cut six pieces of fleece fabric about 10 × 5cm. For each seam sample, place two pieces of fabric right sides (RS) together. Sew a line of stitches 1cm in from the edge of the fabric using:

- a small straight stitch (about 2mm long)
- a long straight stitch (about 4mm long)
- a zig-zag stitch 2mm long and 2mm wide.

C

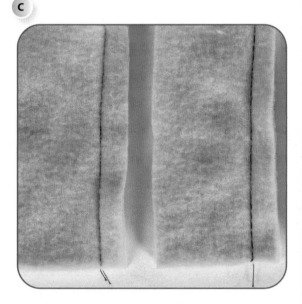

Test the seams in turn by gently stretching them to see if they will 'give' or stretch with the fleece fabric (do not overdo it!)

Help!

D

Which is the right side of my fleece?

Some fleece fabric only has pile on one side. On double-sided fleece fabric look carefully to see which side looks the fluffiest. If you are using patterned fleece the design will look fuzzy on the wrong side.

The top layer of fleece stretched when I was sewing it!

You need to use pins to hold the layers of fleece together. If you put the pins at right angles to the direction you are sewing you can sew over them.

Safety tip – take care to sew very slowly as you go over a pin. If you go too fast and the needle hits the pin it could break off and fly up.

The ends of my stitching are coming undone!

Always start and end a seam with about three reverse stitches to stop this happening.

Plenary

It is important to think about the function of the product you are designing. Designers need to choose a fabric that has the right properties to match the function of the product.

Always do some practice sewing on the fabric you are going to use to make your product. This will help you find out about the working characteristics of the fabric and what processes are suitable to use.

Fun fleece

Objectives

In this lesson you will:

- think about different ways a basic hat style can be altered to make it different
- design and manufacture a prototype fleece hat.

Key words

hem   a way of finishing the edge of a piece of fabric

facing   a separate piece of fabric used to finish the edge of part of a product

DMA Kids and Co.

Kids and Co. is a company that wishes to increase its market share of teenage fashion. The company currently produces a range of winter hats. Two of its basic styles have been very popular and easy to manufacture in quantity. The company wants to use these basic styles in its new winter range. Kids and Co.'s fabric supplier has a range of patterned and plain fleece fabrics, which it wants to use to produce an updated range that would appeal to young teenagers.

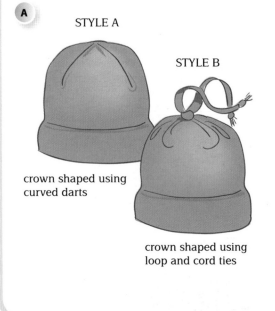

A

STYLE A

STYLE B

crown shaped using curved darts

crown shaped using loop and cord ties

Design brief

Design and make a prototype fun fleece hat that would appeal to the younger teenage market. Before you start designing, think about the ways you could make your hat different to the basic style, the ways you could finish the cut edges, and the extra components you could add to it.

Make it different!

Designers often make different versions of the same basic style by:

- using different fabrics
- using more than one colour of fabric
- adding extra features to the basic style
- adding decoration to the fabric.

Try out some of these ideas to make the basic hat styles different.

Fleece cords

Cut strips of fleece fabric about 1–1.5 cm wide and stretch them. The fabric will roll back on itself to form a cord. Because the fabric does not fray you do not need to neaten the edges of the strip.

Fleece tassles

Look at the diagrams in **B** and follow the instructions below to make fleece tassles.

1 Cut several strips of fleece about 1cm wide (or slightly narrower).

2 Hand stitch the strips together at their middles.

3 Fold the strips in half and stitch the bottom of the tassle together.

B

1

2

3

Finishing the bottom edge

Do not leave this decision until the end; the method you choose should be thought about while you are developing the design of your hat. The type of finish you decide to use will influence the shape of the pattern pieces you make before you cut out your fabric.

Hems

A **hem** is an easy way to finish the lower edge of a hat. The hem allowance is turned to the inside of your hat and stitched in place. Remember to add the depth of the hem to your pattern pieces before cutting them out.

If you make a very deep hem this can be used to form a turn-back edge at the bottom of your hat.

Facing

A **facing** is similar to a hem but it is made from a separate piece of fabric cut to the same length as the lower edge of your hat. A facing can also be used to form a contrasting turn-back at the bottom of your hat.

Cuff

This is rather like the edge you get at the lower edge, neck and wrists of a sweatshirt. A cuff can be made in the same colour or a contrasting colour.

 Fleece hats made from the basic hat styles

FPT Stitching and finishing

1   You will need a stretchy stitch when sewing a hem on your hat because the fabric will need to stretch. You could use an elastic zigzag stitch. This is sometimes called a three-step zigzag stitch because the zigzag is made from three small straight stitches. Try out this stitch on a piece of fleece fabric (see diagram **D**).

2   Try out some of the different methods of finishing the bottom edge of your hat. You could do this by modelling them on a smaller scale.

Plenary

Making changes to existing products or basic styles can be a good way of developing new products. You will need to work out how the different parts of your design will be constructed when you are developing your design ideas. This will help you to work out the shapes of the fabric pieces you need and the order in which to put the pieces together.

Stay cool

Objectives

In this lesson you will:
- find out how fabrics help to keep you cool
- investigate cotton fabrics.

Key words

evaporation   when liquid water turns into vapour

A

Being cool is not just about wearing the right clothes! It is about choosing clothes that will help your body stay at the right temperature and be comfortable. To be comfortable, we need to maintain our body temperature at 37°C. When the weather is hot or when you take part in active sport or exercise, or even when you are just sitting in a hot room, you begin to feel uncomfortable because your body heat rises.

Your body is able to get rid of this extra heat in two ways:
- through the blood vessels that are close to the surface of the skin
- by releasing sweat from the pores in your skin.

Try this. Lick the back of your finger and hold it up in the air. Your finger will start to feel cold. This is because as the moisture on your finger evaporates it takes the heat away from your skin and has a cooling effect. This is why you feel cold when you get out of a swimming pool or the shower, even if the air temperature around you is warm.

When you choose clothes to wear for sport or in hot conditions you need them to be made from fabrics that will soak up (absorb) the sweat from your body or let it evaporate. In this unit we will be looking closely at sports tops.

Think about it!

1   **TS** Think back to what you have learned about fibre properties in Unit 2. Which fibres are good at absorbing moisture?

2   Look at the label inside your PE shirt. What fibre(s) is the fabric made from?

3   Look at some more sports tops in catalogues. What fibre(s) are these made from?

4   a) Which fibres are most frequently used for sports clothes?

    b) Which was the most used natural fibre?

    c) Which was the most used manufactured fibre?

When you have carried out activities 1–4 in the Think about it! box, you will find that the most frequently used natural fibre is cotton. Although it has been around for centuries it is still one of the

Calico   Towelling   Lawn   Printed twill

Single jersey   Denim

B   *Examples of fabrics made from cotton*

C   *The Cotton USA Mark provides customers with strong reassurance that the products they are buying are of the highest quality.*

Think about it!

1   (TS) Look at the different cotton fabrics shown in photo **B**. What products could they be made into?

2   (FPT) Collect samples of different types of fabrics made from cotton. Produce a table with:
- a sample of the fabrics
- a description of the fabrics
- what textile products they could be made into.

3   (ICT) (ABC) (TS) Find out more about cotton by searching the Internet. You can start by using the following website: www.heinemann.co.uk/hotlinks. Use the information you have collected to produce a 'cotton factfile' giving information about:
- where cotton plants are grown
- how the cotton fibres are harvested and turned into yarns
- the properties of cotton fibres
- products that are made from cotton fabrics.

most common fibres in the textile industry. Cotton fibres are very versatile and can be made into lots of different fabrics.

Mixing it!

When you were looking at the labels and in the catalogues for fibres used in sports tops you probably found that some tops were made from more than one fibre such as cotton and polyester fibres. The polyester fibres help to make the fabric easier to care for; they do not crease as much as cotton fibres so the garment will need less ironing and the cotton fibres still make the garment comfortable to wear.

Plenary

We feel comfortable when our body temperature is normal. Clothes that contain cotton fibres are particularly good at helping you to keep your cool!

Stay cool with modern fabrics!

Objectives

In this lesson you will find out about modern fabrics that have been specially designed to keep you cool.

Key words

breathable fabrics	fabrics that move perspiration away from our bodies and out through our clothing
wicking	the process of transporting moisture along a fibre

When you were investigating the fibres that sports tops are made from, you probably found that some of them were made from polyester or polyamide. This might seem a little strange as both these fibres are very poor at absorbing moisture. You have just found out that to stay cool, you need fabrics that are made from absorbent fibres!

Modern technology has meant that synthetic fibres can now be made so that the fabric is breathable. This means that moisture from your body can escape through the fabric and evaporate. One of the main principles behind **breathable fabrics** is a process called **wicking**. This means that moisture can travel along the fibres and away from the body.

Synthetic fibres, like polyamide and polyester, are produced by forcing a liquid fibre solution through a spinneret. Textile technologists can change the cross-section of synthetic fibres by altering the shape of the holes in the spinneret. Synthetic fibres with groves along their length will allow moisture to travel along them. Look at diagram **A**.

A

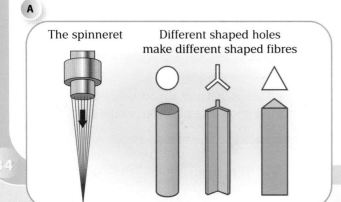

The spinneret — Different shaped holes make different shaped fibres

B

only by DuPont

C

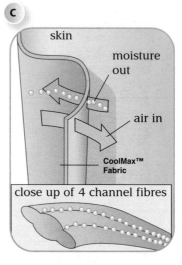

skin

moisture out

air in

CoolMax™ Fabric

close up of 4 channel fibres

Coolmax® is a fabric made from polyester fibres that have a special four-channel cross-section. Moisture from the body can quickly travel along the groves in the fibres away from the skin to the outer layer of the fabric where it can evaporate. Coolmax® is used to make T-shirts, singlets, jerseys, socks, running tights, golf shirts, bodywear and sports bras.

Although cotton fabric is good at absorbing moisture, it also takes quite a long time to dry, which could become uncomfortable. Tactel Aquator® is a two-layer fabric made from an inner layer of Tactel and an outer layer of cotton (diagram **D**). Body moisture is quickly

D

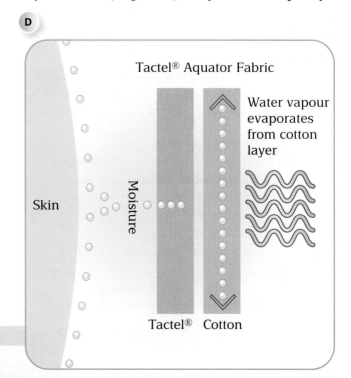

Tactel® Aquator Fabric

Water vapour evaporates from cotton layer

Skin

Moisture

Tactel®   Cotton

wicked away from the body through the Tactel® layer and into the cotton layer where it can evaporate.

There are many different brand names for breathable fabrics that work using the principles described on page 34. Adidas® use a synthetic fabric called Climalite® for many of their sports-clothes (see **E** and **F**). Reebok® use a fabric called Hydromove®. Maxit Designs® use a fabric called Cottonwique® for their Eliminator range of garments.

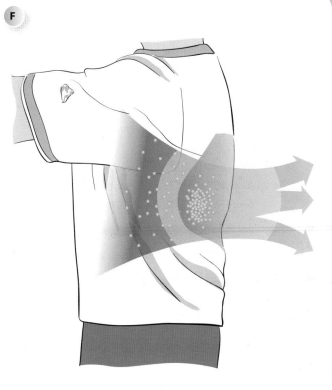

F

E

G *Darren Campbell: it is very important for top athletes and sports personalities to have clothing that keeps them comfortable.*

'I don't know the technical reason for wearing specific fabrics, but I do know that sportswear companies such as my own, Fila, spend a lot of money researching and developing the material we wear. The priority for me is that it is light to wear and fits well to allow freedom of movement when I run. Because the longest distance I run is 200m, I don't really feel the need for a fabric that soaks up the sweat, but this is a factor in my training clothes.'

Darren Campbell

Think about it!

1 **FPT** Collect samples of fabrics made from:
   - 100% cotton
   - a polyester/cotton blend
   - 100% polyester.

   Carry out a drying test to compare how quickly each fabric dries.

2 **ABC** Record and comment on your results.

3 **ICT** Find out more about the branded breathable fabrics described in this section using the Internet.

4 **ABC** **CZ** Produce a magazine advertisement or promotional leaflet for a branded sports top that would appeal to the teenage market. The advertizement should explain why it is 'cool' to wear the top.

Plenary

Technological developments in fibre and fabric production have provided us with a range of different modern fabrics. Some of these are specifically designed to keep us comfortable when taking part in active sports.

A splash of colour 1

Objectives

In this lesson you will:

- learn how to produce a dye bath
- learn how to complete a variety of techniques to apply colour to fabric using a liquid dye
  - ○ tie die
  - ○ batik
  - ○ spray painting
  - ○ direct painting.

Key words

dye	a liquid form of colour used on fabrics
dye bath	the dye and the container
fixative	the chemicals that react with the dye to ensure the colour is permanently held in the fabric
resist technique of dyeing	the dye is prevented from colouring some parts of a fabric

In this section you are designing a promotional T-shirt for an environmentally-friendly company called PrintTex. Pages 40–1 outline the different methods you could use to add your logo design to the T-shirt.

Choosing a fabric to use

When using a liquid **dye**, the best fabrics to use are those made from natural fibres. Cotton is ideal as it absorbs moisture readily and will therefore absorb the dye. Calico is a good choice for all of these techniques.

Making a dye bath

Dye baths are used for tie dyeing and batik. Powdered dye, **fixative** and salt are measured out accurately according to the manufacturer's instructions, and then dissolved in hot water. This solution is poured into a large container. The dye and the container together are called a dye bath. The items to be dyed must be wet before being placed

into the dye bath. The dying takes place during the first ten minutes of the process, and the fabric must be kept moving in the dye bath. Use a large plastic spoon or glass rod to stir the fabric in the dye bath. Plastic and glass do not absorb dye and can therefore be used again and again.

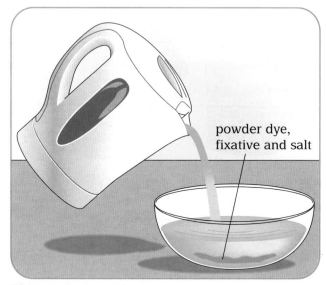

powder dye, fixative and salt

A   *Containers used for dye baths need to be non-absorbent – glass and plastic are ideal materials*

Tie dyeing

Tie dye is a **resist technique of dyeing**. The fabric is tied and then dyed. The dye cannot penetrate the fabric where it is tied, and the base colour is left. Many different patterns can be created in this way (see **B**).

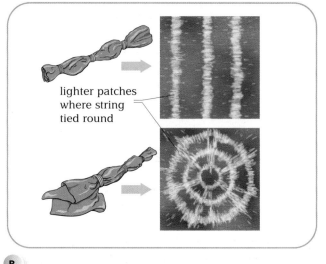

lighter patches where string tied round

B   *Tie dyeing and the results*

Batik

Batik is where wax is applied to the fabric. The fabric is then submerged in the dye bath or painted onto the fabric. The dye cannot penetrate the fabric underneath the wax. Batik designs are built up by applying several layers of wax and dyeing the fabric in different dye baths; the colours mix on the fabric to create different colours. When the wax cracks on the fabric the dye creeps in and gives the characteristic crackled effect of batik. Ironing the fabric helps to fix the dye and removes the wax at the same time.

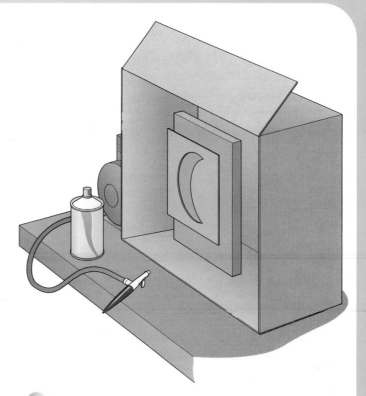

D Spray painting equipment

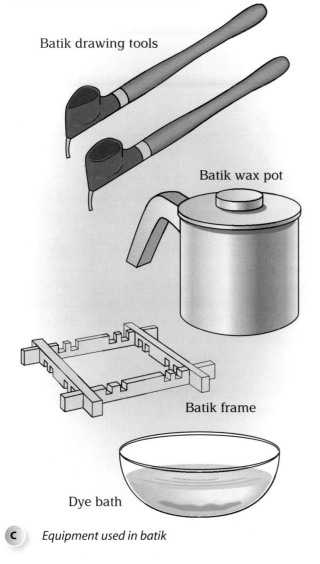

Batik drawing tools

Batik wax pot

Batik frame

Dye bath

C Equipment used in batik

Stencilling by spray painting

Spray painting involves spraying the dye onto the fabric, using a water spray container or a diffuser. If you have access to an air compressor, this will give a more professional finish. Stencils are used to ensure the dye goes where it needs to in order to produce a pattern.

Direct painting

Dye is painted directly onto the fabric using a paint brush or other implement. The dyes are then fixed by ironing.

Think about it!

1 **CZ** **CT** Working in groups, produce a presentation (a display or a PowerPoint presentation) about one of the techniques for adding colour to fabric – tie dye, batik, spray painting or stencilling.

2 **ABC** Give the presentation to your teaching group. The presentation must include instructions on how to complete the technique and include whether it is suitable for batch production, one-off production or mass production. Gather your group's comments about the advantages and disadvantages of each technique.

Plenary

Fabrics can be coloured by using liquid dyes. Tie dye, batik, stencilling and spray painting use different systems to prevent the dye going where it is not wanted. These techniques are known as resist methods of adding colour to fabric.

A splash of colour 2

Objectives

In this lesson you will learn how to complete a variety of techniques to apply colour to fabric using inks:

- block printing
- screen printing
- stencilling.

Key words

motif	an image, unit of pattern
printing pad	a spongy pad coated in printing ink used to apply ink to the block
screen	a frame that has a fabric stretched across it
squeegee	a tool that pushes the ink through the screen
organza	a very fine, strong, transparent fabric
printing ink	a thick (viscose) dye

Block printing

Block printing involves covering a printing block with ink and then pressing it onto a fabric. The block has a **motif** or pattern cut into it. The raised part of the block is what prints the design. You will need a **printing pad** (a piece of felt soaked in the dye) to apply the ink to the block and a soft surface to print on. A natural fabric such as calico works well with this method.

The block is pressed onto the printing pad to coat it with ink, and then pressed on to the fabric to reveal the pattern. This process is repeated as many times as is required. The block can be arranged in a number of different ways to create patterns (see **B**).

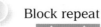

B Block repeat   Brick repeat

Half drop repeat   Random repeat

Screen printing

Screen printing involves pushing ink through a **screen**. A stencil is used to create the design, which is printed in layers. Each layer of printing represents a single colour in the design. A design can be made up of many colours or just a few. Each layer of colour must fit into the other layers of colour used in the design. The matching up of the layers is the tricky part of the technique, and requires skill and accuracy when producing the stencil. It takes a lot of time to prepare the stencils accurately, but the printing process is fairly quick.

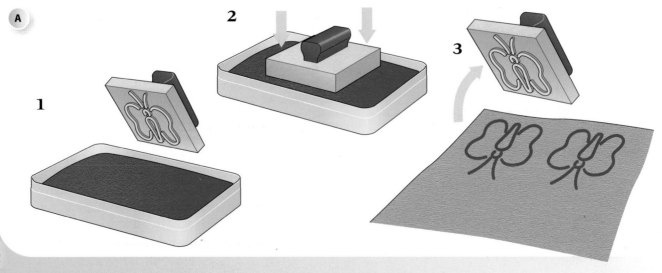

A

1

2

3

FPT Screen printing

For this FPT you will need a screen, a **squeegee**, a stencil of the design you want (start with a single colour shape to get the feel of screen printing and progress to several stencils and colours and more complex designs later), and a printing pad.

Step 1 Prepare the screen

Ensure the fabric (a cotton or polyester **organza** fabric) is stretched tightly across the frame and held firmly in place. A staple gun holds the fabric in place.

Step 2 Attach the stencil

The fabric must be stretched very tightly across the frame. Attach the stencil to the centre of the frame on the outside of the screen, using gummed tape (see diagram **C**). Cover the space around the stencil with gummed tape to prevent the ink going through the screen when you print.

C

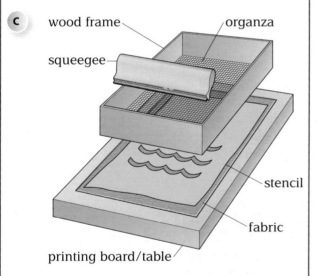

wood frame
organza
squeegee
stencil
fabric
printing board/table

Step 3 Printing on the fabric

Place the screen on top of the fabric you wish to print onto. Make sure the fabric is stretched tightly on the printing surface using masking tape. This ensures you achieve a clear print.

Step 4 Printing

Spoon some **printing ink** across the top edge of the screen and, using the squeegee, pull the ink down across the screen The squeegee works best at an angle of 45° to the screen. Carefully lift the screen, to reveal the design printed onto the fabric. If additional colours are to be added then the first set of inks must be dry before the second colour is added.

Stencilling

Stencilling adds colour to a fabric using a stencil. Cutting certain shapes out of a special non-absorbent material creates a stencil. The stencil is placed on top of the fabric and the ink applied with either a stencil brush or a sponge brush (see **D**).

D

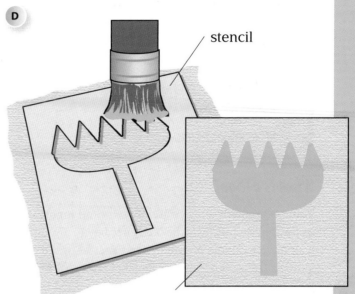

stencil

finished motif

Labels and logos

In this lesson you will learn:
- what a logo is
- how to produce an effective logo.

Key words

logo a symbol that represents a company or an organization

What is a logo?

You are probably very aware of the brand **logos** used in designer clothing – the 'designer label'. You may well have paid lots of money for a special brand of T-shirt or trousers because of its label. You will have paid for the image or style that is represented by the logo of that product.

A logo is designed to communicate information. A logo frequently includes an illustration of the company's product or service or an abstract pattern, sometimes created from geometric shapes, which suggests the image or style of the company. The secret of a successful logo is keeping the design simple to communicate vital information effectively in an interesting and novel way.

Designing a logo

A logo must represent the image or style of a company or service. The logo must appeal to the customers or clients the company intends to attract. The name or initials of the company are often included in the logo. Long names make a logo difficult to read and initials can require a great deal of promotion to establish. For these reasons companies tend to favour short names such as Gap, Next, Chanel, Dior, Jig Saw, Vans. I am sure if you stop and think for a minute, you will be able to list more companies with short and straightforward names.

Colours

The colours used in logos play a very special part. Pastel colours tend to suggest quality, while reds and yellows suggest price is important. The fewer colours used in a logo means it is less expensive to produce. Techniques such as screen printing make the logo quick to manufacture.

A

WOOLMARK

Macmillan *cancer relief*

British Heart Foundation

PUMA

Lettering and logos

The different styles of a font used in a logo convey very different messages.

Look at the range of styles of lettering used in the representation of the Google.com logo in **C**. Can you see how the style of letters affects the final logo?

Tahoma –a modern feel

Italics – suggest speed

Upper and Lower case lettering – this is generally easier to read because each word has it's own unique shape

B *Can you see that the colours and style of letters in these logos alter the feel of the company?*

Think about it!

1 **TS** **ABC** **ICT** Using the Internet, make an electronic collection of various charity logos.

  a) Select your five favourite logos.

  b) Group these logos according to the colours they have used.

  c) Write a short description about the image of the charity portrayed by each logo.

2 **D** **TS** Select a charity you support and update its existing logo. You will need to consider the following:

  ● the colours

  ● the style of lettering

  ● what images could be simplified to convey the correct visual impression of the charity.

Plenary

Logos are a very powerful way of communicating style and an image. The type of line, the style of the font, the patterns or pictures and colours all play a major role in developing an effective logo.

Who is it for?

Objectives

In this lesson you will:

- learn that designers use customer profiles when designing products
- develop an image board for a target market.

Key words

target market	the group of customers that a product is designed for
customer profile	common factors of customers in the target market
image board	a visual representation of the customer/target market

Which one would you buy?

When you buy a product you are faced with many different types to choose from; the product you decide to choose will probably be very different to one that would be chosen by someone else.

Think about it!

TS Look at the products in **A**. They are all suitable for holding money. Discuss the following questions in class.

a) Which one would you buy? Why?

b) Who would buy the other products in the picture? Why? (What are the clues?)

B

When you design products for a **target market** you have to think about what the customer would like – not what you like! In industry, designers develop a **customer profile** of their target market. This means finding out about the type of person who will buy the product they are designing (**B**).

To get a 'feel' of their target market and to help them stay focused while designing a product, designers often produce an **image board** (look at **C**). This is a collection of images that are connected with the type of person they are designing for, such as food, products, places, words, colours and so on. Image boards are often produced using pictures from magazines and catalogues. An electronic image board can be put together using images from the Internet and Clip Art.

DMA Bag It

'Bag It' is a company that specializes in the production of small containers for a whole range of technological products, from digital cameras to personal organizers and sunglasses. The marketing department of the company wish to introduce an exciting new range. They would like to have a 'zipped container' that could be decorated in different ways so that it would appeal to a number of different clients.

Your task is to:

● develop and manufacture the standard zipped container

● develop a range of ideas to show how the prototype could be adapted to suit a range of target markets

● produce one of your designs for a specific target market.

As part of your research for this assignment, you need to investigate the different types of customer your container could be manufactured for. You could do this by carrying out a survey to find out about customer lifestyle, such as their likes and dislikes, their hobbies and interests. You will need to think carefully about what you want to find out and the type of questions you will need to ask.

Think about it!

1 **TS** Look at the image board in **C** and discuss these questions.

a) What type of person do you think is represented?

b) What clues are there in the image board?

2 **TS** **ICT** Identify three different target markets.

a) Produce a questionnaire to help you to find out about the different target customers.

b) Use the answers to your survey to help you produce an image board for one or more of your target customers. If possible, produce an electronic image board.

Plenary

It is important to think about the customer you are designing for. Producing an image board will help you understand your customer and the product you are working on. Remember to refer to your image board while you are designing your product.

Getting the shape right

In this lesson you will:

● understand how product analysis can be used to produce patterns for textile products

● consider how patterns can be used to produce products for different functions and users.

Key words

disassembly taking a product apart to see how it has been constructed

You will need to get some ideas for the shape and size of your zipped container. One of the things that will influence this is the function it will be used for – that is, what it is designed to hold. Sometimes the same shape of container can be made in different sizes to hold different things. Look at the containers in **A**. They are all based on a rectangle shape, but they are different sizes and would be used by different customers for different functions!

Taking it apart

Whatever type of textile product you are making, you need to start with a pattern for the different fabric pieces. One way of developing a pattern is to analyze how existing similar products have been made. Designers and manufacturers often do this to find out about the products made by their competitors.

Textile products can be disassembled (taken apart) to find how the product was made and the different fabric shapes used in its' construction. **Dissasembly** can be time consuming and not always acceptable! With simple products it is often possible to carry out a **virtual disassembly**.

This means analyzing the product very carefully and taking measurements to work out the shapes it has been made from. Look at **B** to see how a pencil case has been disassembled.

It is very important to work out and draw the pattern shapes carefully to make sure that they will all fit together. You will need to use your mathematical knowledge to make sure the pattern pieces are accurate! Pattern drafting programs can be very helpful when making patterns.

A

B

Patterns are often made from paper so that they can be pinned to a single or double layer of fabric. If a pattern is going to be used a lot it can be made from card. Card pattern pieces are placed on the top layer of fabric and can be drawn round using tailors chalk. On a card pattern a notch is marked by cutting a small 'V' into the seam allowance. A small hole can be punched in the card to show the position of a balance mark.

All the same size

Making a pattern for a product will enable you to accurately cut out the fabric pieces for any number of identical products. When you sew the fabric pieces together it is also important to be accurate! You must use the correct seam allowance included in the pattern. If you sew a narrower seam the product will end up larger. If you sew a wider seam your product will end up smaller.

The same but different

Once a pattern has been worked out, it can be used to produce more identical products. The same pattern can also be used to produce products that are the same size and shape but for different customers

and/or for different functions. This is achieved by using other:

- types of fabric
- colours of fabric
- decorative techniques.

Think about it!

1 **PA** Analyse a collection of small fabric containers with zip fastenings to find out what fabric shapes they have been made from.

2 **CT** Select one of the containers you have analysed and produce the pattern pieces needed to cut out the fabric shapes. This could be done using a pattern drafting program.

3 **FPT** Use the pattern pieces you have made to manufacture a prototype container.

Plenary

Analysing existing products is a good way to find out how they have been constructed. Many new products can be developed by adapting the patterns used to make existing products. The same basic style can be used to make the product suitable for a different function or target customer.

Gaining inspiration!

Objectives

In this lesson you will:

- learn where to find a starting point or inspiration
- learn how to develop a starting point to create a pattern or design.

Key words

pattern a sequence of recurring shapes or images

To make your container appeal to different customers you could decorate the fabric by adding a motif or a **pattern**.

Where do I start?

Inspiration does not just 'fall from the sky' but is developed from a starting point by the designer. The secret is finding a source that will interest you, the designer, and then to develop it further in a variety of ways so that it will appeal to your customer.

There are many different sources of inspiration for your design work.

- Nature: colour schemes, shapes, and patterns found in nature, such as the markings of a zebra or the patterns found in rock strata.

- Words: bubble, refraction, crystalline, liquid – some words create images in the mind, which can be starting points or ideas that can be worked on.
- History: designers from the past, products from the past such as jewellery – brooches, necklaces, pendants and china.
- Existing products/designs on fabric, wall furnishings and so on.
- The media: television and films can all spark initial ideas.
- Poetry can provide visual pictures that can be transferred into images.
- Music can inspire colours, markings and shapes – covers from records, audiotapes, CDs can also inspire you.
- The man-made world we live in: wrought iron, gates, balconies, patterns on manhole covers, brickwork, stained glass windows and so on.

You can probably see that starting points can come from anything that you find interesting. Designers produce sketchbooks full of images, drawings and notes and use these to help them think of new ideas when they are designing.

Think about it!

TS Begin developing a design sketchbook by collecting different pictures and images using the starting points suggested on this page. Organize your sketchbook so that you can add extra images and drawings later on.

A

B

How do I take the inspiration further?

There are many different things that you can do with the images you have collected, whether they are line drawings or coloured pictures. You could:

- alter the size of the image by enlarging or reducing it
- use the colours from the image
- turn the image upside down or back to front
- mirror the image
- overlay the image shape on itself to create additional shapes and patterns.

Think about it!

For the following design tasks you will need an image or picture.

1 **FPT** This activity can help you to select an effective colour scheme that could be applied to any design or pattern. Look at **C**.

- Choose a picture and collect threads that match the colours in the picture.
- Organize the threads from light to dark.
- Take a piece of card and place some double-sided tape along the back.
- Wrap the threads around the card; the double-sided tape will hold them in position.

C

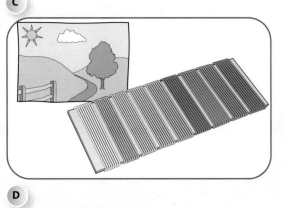

D

2 **FPT** This activity can help you to create interesting abstract designs. You will need a line drawing or a picture from your sketchbook (see **D**).

- Select an image.
- Cut it up!
- Rearrange the pieces in any order you like to create some abstract shapes and images.

3 **FPT** This activity can also help you to create interesting abstract designs (see **E**).

- Select an area from a drawing or picture.
- Reproduce the portion of the image or picture you have selected.
- Enlarge it or reduce it in size to create a random abstract pattern.

E

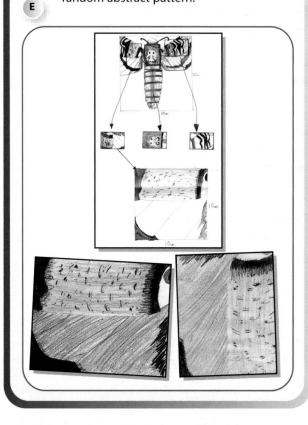

Plenary

Remember the word 'pattern' is used here to refer to a repeated design that can be applied to a fabric. Get into the habit of collecting images and making drawings of things that appeal to you and keep them in a design sketchbook. This will be a useful source of inspiration when you need ideas for other design assignments.

What a transformation!

Objectives

In this lesson you will learn:

- how to use transfer techniques to add colour to a fabric
- how fabric can be digitally printed using a personal computer.

Key words

'Cool peel' transfer paper   a special paper which is fed through a colour printer

Transfer printing

One way of adding motifs or patterns to fabric is to use transfer printing. Transfer crayons, inks and **'cool peel' transfer paper** are techniques that transfer a design to fabric very quickly. These techniques allow all the colours of a design to be added at the same time. They all require heat to transfer the design and the image is reversed when transferred to the fabric.

Transfer crayons and inks work in the same way. The design is coloured or painted on to paper. The paper is then placed on to the fabric with the coloured side down. Heat is then applied and the design is transferred to the fabric. Transfer techniques work best on synthetic fabrics. The more synthetic fibre the fabric contains, the stronger the final colours become.

On 'cool peel' transfer paper the design is computer printed onto the special transfer paper. Heat is applied to transfer the design onto the fabric. The backing paper must be quite cool before it is removed to reveal the image which has been transferred to the fabric (**A**).

Transfer printing is widely used in industry to print fabrics. It is a relatively new and quick method of adding colours to a fabric. The design is printed onto paper and then the fabric and paper are passed between heated rollers. The heat combined with the pressure from the rollers transfers the design to the fabric. The paper that has been used to print the fabric is often cut up into sheets and sold to florists, or made into paper bags.

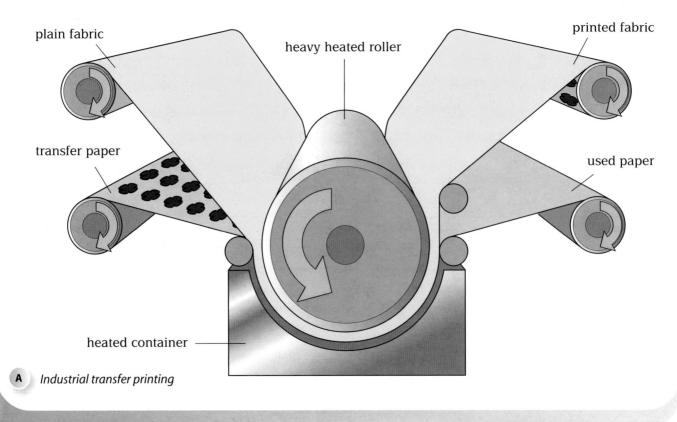

plain fabric

heavy heated roller

printed fabric

transfer paper

used paper

heated container

A *Industrial transfer printing*

🖰 *Transfer printing*

Collect a selection of florist's paper and coloured paper bags. Carry out the following experiment to see if they have been made from transfer printing paper.

1   Cut out a piece of paper and place it coloured side down onto a piece of white polyester or cotton fabric.

2   Iron over the paper for about 30 seconds.

3   Remove the paper to see if the dye has been transferred to the fabric.

Digital printing

In digital printing fabrics are printed directly from the computer. The design on the screen is printed onto the fabric. The fabric used in this process is specially prepared to accept the special computer printer fabric dyes. This means it is possible to design a fabric on screen, press the print button, and the design is printed on fabric. Using this digital technique, fabrics can be easily produced in smaller amounts without the vast costs of expensive screen printing frames or rollers which have been used in the past. Fabric widths are restricted to the width of the printers.

It is possible to digitally print onto fabric in the classroom too. A very simple way to do this without using expensive equipment is to use a product called 'Bubble Jet Set' (see **B**). All you have to do is soak your fabric (usually cotton) in the special solution, let it dry, iron it onto waxed freezer paper and feed it through your standard PC printer! This technique can be used to produce fabric in A4 or A3 size, depending on the printer you have.

Plenary

Both transfer and digital printing techniques are quick and easy to carry out and can transform a piece of white or light-coloured plain fabric. Combining these methods of adding colour to fabric with other techniques like quilting or decorative machine stitching can produce even more interesting ideas.

B

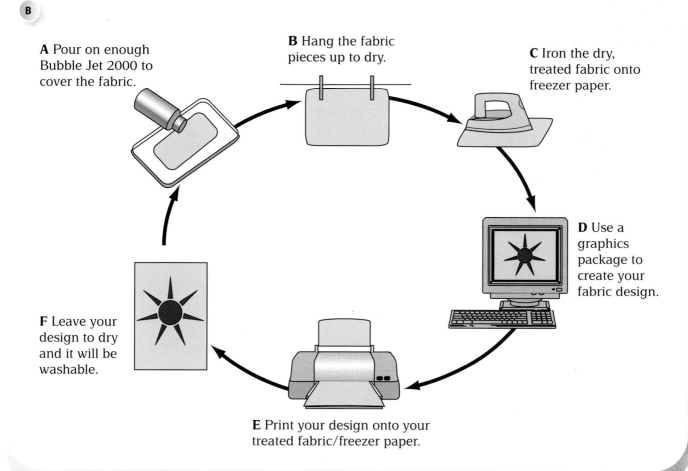

A Pour on enough Bubble Jet 2000 to cover the fabric.

B Hang the fabric pieces up to dry.

C Iron the dry, treated fabric onto freezer paper.

D Use a graphics package to create your fabric design.

E Print your design onto your treated fabric/freezer paper.

F Leave your design to dry and it will be washable.

Be specific!

Objectives

In this lesson you will learn about different types of specification and when and why they are used.

Key words

criteria rules or points against which something is judged or checked

prioritize decide what is most and/or least important

The word specification comes from the word specific, which means being precise or exact. In Design and Technology we use several different types of specification.

Design specification

This is a list of specific things about a product that a designer has to keep in mind while designing. The things listed in a design specification will vary according to the type of product being designed. So, for example, things that are important when designing a soft toy for a child will be different to the things that are important when designing a tent! To help you write a detailed design specification, you need to think about the points in **A**.

The list of items in a specification are called **criteria**. Some criteria will be more important than others; these are essential criteria. Other criteria may be less important; these are desirable but not necessarily essential. When designing your product you will need to **prioritize** the criteria. Sometimes this means having to make compromises.

A

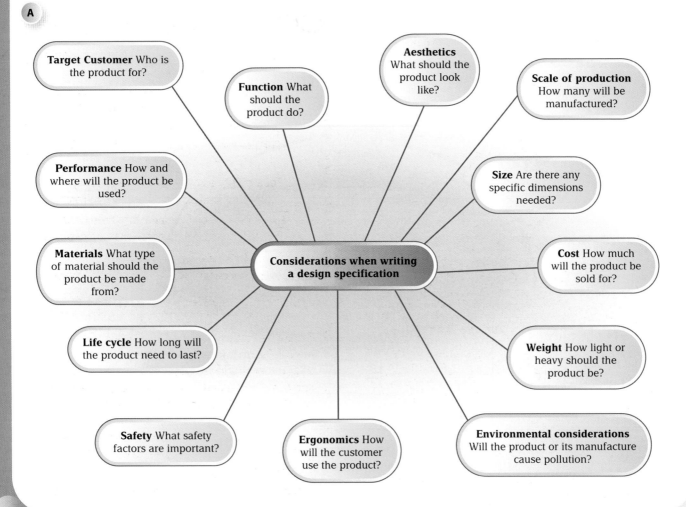

Target Customer Who is the product for?

Function What should the product do?

Aesthetics What should the product look like?

Scale of production How many will be manufactured?

Performance How and where will the product be used?

Size Are there any specific dimensions needed?

Materials What type of material should the product be made from?

Considerations when writing a design specification

Cost How much will the product be sold for?

Life cycle How long will the product need to last?

Weight How light or heavy should the product be?

Safety What safety factors are important?

Ergonomics How will the customer use the product?

Environmental considerations Will the product or its manufacture cause pollution?

Fabric specification

This is a list of criteria giving the important properties the fabric needs in order for it to be suitable for the product. A fabric specification should include information about functional properties and aesthetic properties.

- Functional properties include how the fabric performs – absorbency, strength.
- Aesthetic properties include how the fabric looks and feels – they are the sorts of things that give textiles products their 'customer appeal'.

Sometimes the criteria in a fabric specification are included in the design specification.

Product specification

This is sometimes referred to as a production plan or components list. It contains the technical information that is needed to manufacture a product. It is often set out as a chart and includes details such as:

- a line drawing of the product showing front and back views
- the dimensions of the product
- the components needed to complete the product
- the fabric the product is to be made from
- tolerance levels – the margin of acceptable variation on measurements.

Producing a product specification can be a useful way of recording information when you analyse existing products.

Manufacturing specification

This is used to organise how a product should be made in a factory and is sometimes called an operations breakdown or operations plan as the making of the product is 'broken down' into a number of operations or stages. This can be set out as a work schedule or flow chart.

Product and manufacturing specifications are used to make sure that all products are made to the same quality when more than one product is being made.

Depending on the size of the company or product, different companies will use different types of charts to record the technical information about a product. Sometimes the information in the product and manufacturing specifications will be included in a single chart.

Producing these types of specification will help you to work out what materials and components you need for your product and the best order to construct it.

Think about it!

1. **TS** Produce a design specification that would help you to design the following products.
   a) For a primary school student: a container to hold a pen, twelve crayons, a 15cm ruler, a rubber and a sharpener.
   b) For a teenager: a case to carry twenty-five CDs when visiting friends.
   c) For a cyclist: a container to carry money (notes and loose change) and credit cards.
2. **TS** Prioritize the criteria for the three products in question 1 to identify those that are essential and those that are desirable.

Plenary

Make sure that you use the different specifications in your Design and Technology projects. Use your design specification to help you when you design and evaluate the performance of your product. Use your fabric specification to help you select the best fabrics for your product. Use your product and manufacturing specifications to help you produce a good quality product and evaluate the quality of your manufacturing.

B *Analysing existing products will help you to make decisions about your own*

Making more than one

Objectives

In this lesson you will::

- understand about scales of productiont
- find out about how batches of products can be made.

Key words

scale of production	the quantity of products to be manufactured
production system	the organization of manufacturing products

Products can be made in different quantities from individual products to batches. A batch of products is a fixed number of identical products. Batches vary from a small batch of just a few products (limited editions, kit for a team, boutique clothes) to large batches of hundreds or even thousands (chain store fashions, school uniforms).

The quantity of products made is called the **scale of production**. Organizing the way products are made depends on the scale of production. The different methods of organizing the manufacture of products are called **production systems**.

Make-through production

This is where one-off products are made by one person from start to finish. The people making one-off products have to be highly skilled, as they need to carry out many different processes on various different products.

Batch production

Batches of products are usually made by groups of people working together. The processes involved in the manufacture of the product are broken down into a number of specific jobs. Each person involved in the manufacture of the product will carry out a specific process. The number of processes and people producing the product will depend on the number of products being made and the number of processes involved in making the product.

Progressive bundle system

Once the fabric pieces have been cut out, they are bundled together and sent to the sewing room. The machinists sit in rows at their machines. Each group of machinists (a section) works on one process; when this is finished the bundles are stored and then passed on to the next section. The factory manager has to organize how many machinists are needed in each section so that the production line runs smoothly. The machinists are trained to do one specific job; they will be taught new skills depending on what process they have to carry out.

A *The progressive bundle system*

Quick response system

This is sometimes called team working because teams of about eight machinists work together to manufacture batches of products. The machinists work standing up and move from one machine to another to carry out a number of different processes on the product. The team works together to organize which machinist will do each process. They have the satisfaction of seeing the product through from start to finish. Each machinist needs to be skilled at using a number of different machines and carrying out a number of different processes. This system is called a quick response system because it is adaptable – the type of products that each team is making can be changed quickly to meet the needs of the retailers (shops).

B *The quick response system*

📝 Greetings cards

This task will help you to understand how batches of products can be manufactured by groups of people working together.

Small batches of hand-finished greetings cards are often sold in craft centres and art galleries. They are also made in very large batches for companies like Marks and Spencer (look at **C**).

C

1 Design and produce a prototype greeting card that could be batch produced to be sold in a local craft centre.

2 Working as a group, select one of your prototype card designs and produce a batch of twenty identical cards. You will need to:

- produce a product specification for the card
- produce a manufacturing specification listing the different processes involved in making the card
- divide up the making process and allocate each member of your group a task
- prepare the materials and other resources needed
- manufacture your batch of cards
- check the quality of the finished cards against your product specification.

Plenary

When you are making products in school you often produce a one-off or prototype product and make it yourself from start to finish. Remember to think about how your products could be manufactured commercially.

CAD/CAM – machine madness

Objectives

In this lesson you will learn what equipment and techniques are available to help you produce several products that are identical.

Key words

CAD	Computer aided design
stitching template	a template that identifies exactly where the stitching is to be placed
CAM	Computer aided manufacture
CNC	Computer numerical control

DMA Juggling kit

You are required to design and manufacture a juggling kit. The juggling kit consists of a themed bag and several juggling shapes. The focus of this brief is to ensure that the products are all the same size and of good quality.

CAD – using computers to help create patterns and templates

To design and create the profile for the juggling shapes, it would be good to use a **CAD** package which will allow you to design and print out a paper pattern. There are lots of specialized CAD packages for pattern generation that will enable you to produce paper patterns. These patterns/ templates will allow you get the correct shaped fabric time after time. Pattern making has been covered in more detail earlier in the book (see pages 10–11).

If you do not have a specialized CAD package, you could use simple DTP packages or any drawing package such as 2D Designtools to help you to produce a pattern. You must remember whether you have or have not added the seam allowance to the pattern. If you do not include the seam allowance then you have created a **stitching template**. A stitching template will help to stitch a shape

accurately time after time. If you are making several hundred products in your batch, you will need a firm material to make the template from so the shape is not distorted during production from the wear and tear on the template.

A

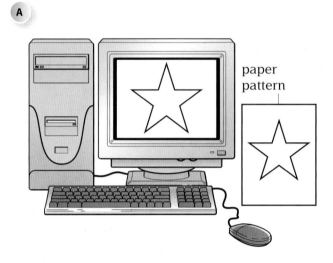

paper pattern

CAM – using machines to decorate fabrics

You can buy specialist embroidery machines that will only do embroidery (**B**), or machines with an embroidery attachment that can be set to do both ordinary sewing and embroidery (**C**). As well as using the designs pre-programmed into the machine,

B

C

you can buy special software so that you can produce your own embroidery designs. The stitch information is transferred onto a special card or disc, which is put into the machine.

When you use a computer to produce a design this is called CAD (Computer Aided Design). When the machine produces the embroidery design this is called **CAM** (Computer Aided Manufacture) because the computer in the machine is controlling the stitching.

CNC embroidery machines

When embroidery designs are stitched on a **CNC** machine, the machine needle stays still and the fabric is moved in a special embroidery hoop,

which is connected to a computer-controlled arm on the machine.

Producing stencils

A plotter and cutter machine can be hooked up to a computer, allowing stencils to be produced (**D**). The stencils can be made from vinyl and ironed on to the product or they can be used to add colour to the fabric either by screen printing or by using a stencil brush or sponging.

Using CAD/CAM equipment produces the same product time after time. It may take time producing the initial template, but generally it only has to be completed once for as many products as you wish to manufacture.

D

Think about it!

1 (TS) Why do you think embroidery designs are embroidered onto flat fabric pieces before a product is assembled?

2 (TS) What are the advantages of using a machine to help you produce more than one of any product?

Plenary

Machines can be used to help produce products that are identical. There are many different machines that complete very different tasks.

CAD equipment helps with the designing of a product. CAM machines help with the manufacturing of the product.

More machines

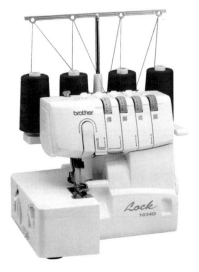

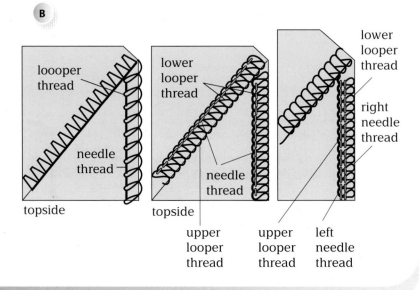

A *Overlockers are much more complicated to thread than an ordinary sewing machine. It is a good idea to leave it threaded up even when it is not in use.*

Sewing machines

The lockstitch sewing machine you use in school can be set to carry out a variety of processes. This is done by setting different types of stitches and using different presser foot attachments.

Industrial lockstitch machines work in the same way as domestic machines, but they need to be much stronger as they work at much higher speeds. There are many types of lockstitch sewing machines used in industry. Each machine is designed to carry out a specific stitch or process.

Overlockers

Look at the stitches that have been used to sew the side seams on a T-shirt or sweatshirt. These have been made using an **overlocker** and look quite different to lockstitch sewing machine stitches (straight stitch machines).

An overlocker looks different and works in a different way to a sewing machine (see **A**). There are two, three or four large reels of thread on the top of the machine, which thread up to one or two needles and one or two loopers underneath the needles (inside the machine). Together the needles and loopers form different types of chain stitches. The overlocker not only sews

fabric pieces together but it also cuts and neatens the edges of the fabric all in one operation. Overlockers are ideal to use when sewing knitted fabrics together as the stitching will stretch with the fabric.

Safety tips

You need to be very careful when you use an overlocker. Keep your fingers away from the blade that cuts the fabric. Be very careful to sew in the right place – you can easily cut off bits of fabric without meaning to, and this will ruin your work!

B

looper thread

needle thread

topside

lower looper thread

needle thread

topside

upper looper thread

lower looper thread

right needle thread

upper looper thread

left needle thread

The domestic sewing machine

Domestic sewing machines can be set to carry out a wide variety of different processes. This is often done by using different types of stitches together with different presser foot attachments.

Zip foot

This is a special foot control that allows the needle to stitch close to the teeth of the zip while the presser foot sits comfortably on the fabric (see **C**).

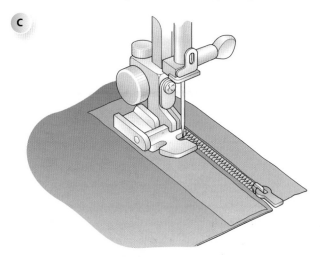

C

Buttonhole foot

Many machines have a special foot that is used to make the stitching of buttonholes easy and accurate. This foot is used together with special stitch settings that are controlled automatically to form the different parts of the buttonhole.

Designing for batch production

When designing for the batch production of a product in industry, there are many areas that need to be considered.

Costs

Various costs need to be taken into account:
- the time taken to make the product
- the materials needed to make the product – the fabrics and the components
- the cost of manufacturing any decorative features such as an embroidered motif, a patch pocket or a belt. (The more colours on an embroidered motif, the more costly the motif is to make. Changing the colour on a machine takes time and this has to be paid for.)

Skills

The skill of the work force will affect the design because the designers have to consider the workers, skills in relation to:
- the shapes used in making the product
- the number of pieces needed to make the product
- the decorative features used on the product
- the choice of fabrics and components because some fabrics are more difficult to work with than others
- the techniques and processes used to construct the product.

Equipment

The equipment available will affect the design through the processes that can or can't be completed.

When designing in school for batch production, you also need to consider the above points so that you can manufacture products within the time frame you have for the project and the facilities available to you, as well as understanding limitations with regard to the manufacturing.

Think about it!

1 **ICT** Find out more about industrial sewing machines by going to the following website and clicking on this activity: www.heinemann.co.uk/hotlinks.

2 **FPT** If you have an overlocker in school, produce a seam sample. Mount your sample and explain how using an overlocker is different to using a lockstitch machine.

3 **TS** Find examples of two different CAM motifs. Which one would be more costly to manufacture than the other? Why?

Plenary

When designing and manufacturing batches of products, it is important to consider cost, skills and the equipment you have available.

When organizing the manufacturing of a batch of products, you could set up each sewing machine to a specific stitch setting required in the making process.

Fabric finishes-the final touch

Key words

handle   what the fabric is like to hold and work with

As you learned earlier, most fabrics are constructed by either knitted woven or bonded methods of manufacture. The way fabrics are made affects the properties the fabrics have. However, after a fabric has been manufactured, it may require a 'finish' to be added to it. The finish will improve the appearance, performance or **handle** of the fabric. A finish could be applied by using mechanical methods, or by applying chemicals. The table in **A** shows how different processes alter the properties of the fabric.

Modern fabrics are constructed from a variety of differently processed fibres (see table **B**). The resulting fabrics have special properties because of the way they have been processed previously.

Type of finish	Description of the finish	Properties affected A – Appearance H – Handle P – Performance
Mechanical		
Brushing	A set of rollers with fine hooks of wire pass over the fabric to brush the surface	A, H
Calendering	Hard heavy rollers pass over the surface of the fabric. This smoothes the surface of the fabric and improves the shine	A, H
Embossing	Engraved rollers are used to create a relief pattern on the surface of the fabric	A
Shrinkage	The fabric is steamed and placed over a vibrating conveyor belt to ensure the fabric does not shrink	P
Pressing	Fabrics are pressed to smooth the surface of the fabric – often used with wool fabrics	A, H
Chemical		
Stain resistant	Stain-resistant substances are applied to the surface of the fabric	P
Water repellent	The fabric is sprayed with silicone to prevent water penetrating the fabric	P
Hygienic	Application of chemicals that hinder the growth of micro-organisms	P
Antistatic	The surface of the fabric is improved to prevent the build up of static charge	P
Flame resistant	Application of a substance that prevents the fabric from easily igniting	P

A   *Finishing fabrics*

B

The name of the fibre	Trade name of the manufactured fibre	Properties of the fibre and resultant fabric
Aramid	Kelvar, Nomex	Extremely flame resistant
Elastane	Lycra, Spandex	Very poor absorbency, very elastic, lightweight, resistant to chemicals
Polyamide	Tactel, Nylon	Extremely strong, good elasticity, melts as it burns, resistant to mould and bacteria, damaged by sunlight
Lyocell	Tencel	Extremely strong, very absorbent, can be shiny or matt

Aftercare of products

Detergents, fabric softeners and using a tumble dryer can all damage fabrics. The ITCL (International Textile Care Labelling) is a code that is used to label textile products. Information about how to care for the product can be found on a label stitched into the product, or it may be printed on the packaging of the product. Other products could have the care label attached to the product using a swing label.

Care labelling

Care labels were designed to help us look after textile products (**C**). Labels are divided into five main sections.

C

Washing

The number on the symbol shows what temperature the product can be washed at. A line underneath the wash symbol shows how vigorous the process can be.

Ironing

The dots inside the iron symbol indicate the hottest temperature the fabric can be ironed at. Three dots represents a high temperature (200 °C) whereas a single dot is the coolest setting(110 °C)

Dry cleaning

The letter inside the circle indicates the types of chemicals that can be used in the cleaning process.

Chlorine

The triangular symbol indicates whether bleach will affect the fabric. This symbol is required for professional laundering where chlorine bleaches may be used.

Drying

A circle inside the square indicates that the fabric can be tumble-dried. A line underneath the square indicates gentle tumbling.

A cross through any symbol indicates that the process is not suitable.

Think about it!

1   **ICT** Use the Internet to help you discover about other modern materials. Produce a scrap book titled 'Modern materials'.

   a) In your scrapbook, include information about as many new and modern materials as you possibly can.

   b) Classify and organize the information you have discovered before starting to produce your scrapbook.

2   **ABC TS** Look at your school jumper, your sweatshirt or your blazer.

   a) Write a full description about how to care for this product.

   b) What are the reasons for caring for the garment in the way you have described?

Plenary

The surface of the fabric (finish) can be adjusted to add properties to the fabric. The finish can improve the appearance or performance of the fabric. Fibres and fabrics need to be cared for correctly and there is a simple symbol system to help do this.

Modern materials

Objectives

In this lesson you will:

- learn about technological developments in the textiles industry
- find out where modern materials are used.

Key words

technical textiles	fibres or fabrics developed for their special performance properties
smart textiles	materials that are able to react to the user or the environment

Question: What do the items in **A** have in common?

Answer: Textiles, of course, but not just in the clothes the people are wearing!

A

The development of manufactured fibres was originally inspired by the need for new and improved fabrics for clothing. During the 1960s, however, the search for new fibres was driven by the need to produce fabrics with improved performance properties for use in the space program.

Fibres and fabrics that are developed with specific performance properties to fulfil a function are referred to as **technical textiles**. Many of today's textile innovations have come from fabrics developed for military use and the medical and cosmetics industries.

Geotextiles

Geotextiles is the name given to textiles materials used in civil engineering. Textiles are widely used in civil engineering for reinforcement, drainage and filtration, such as in road and railway construction, strengthening and protecting embankments and preventing coastal erosion. They are made either as non-woven fabrics or as a woven mesh. Non-woven geotextiles might even have been used underneath your patio or drive or as a weed barrier in your garden!

Medical textiles

Textile items such as bandages and surgeons gowns have been used in medicine for many years. More recently, special textiles have been developed to make replacement body parts such as arteries and veins (**B**).

B

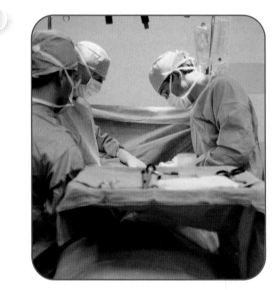

Composite textiles

Composite fabrics are made from two or more fabrics combined together using resins and adhesives. Fibre-reinforced composites are used for car bodies and tyres, tennis rackets, aircraft fuselages, rocket nose cones, helmets, bicycle frames and fishing poles among many other uses.

Smart textiles

Smart textiles respond in some way to their environment, for example, to differences in temperature or light conditions. Smart materials appear to 'think' and some have a 'memory' as they can revert back to their original state.

Sense and react

Memory foam is a material that was first developed for NASA to use in spacecraft seats for astronauts. It reduced the effects of the excessive G-forces experienced during take-off and landing. Memory foam adjusts to the body weight and temperature of the user (**C**). It flows to match the contours of the body and slowly returns to its original shape once the pressure is removed. It is now used in beds, pillows and chairs.

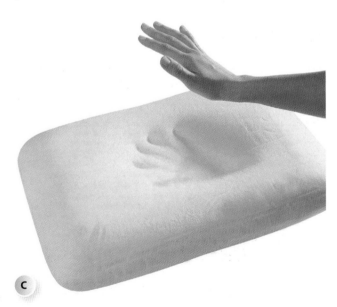

C

Electrical textiles

Electrical circuitry can now be incorporated into garments by using conductive threads knitted or woven into a fabric so they are touch sensitive. You can have a mobile phone in your jacket or tie,

the remote controls to your television in the arm of your chair, or socks that monitor your sporting performance!

D SOFTswitch is a company that makes touch-sensitive and interactive fabrics

Think about it!

1 **TS** **ICT** **ABC** One of the best ways to find up-to-date information about technological developments in fibres and fabrics is to use the Internet.

a) Go to www.heinemann.co.uk/hotlinks and click on this activity to find out more about modern fibres and fabrics.

b) Using ICT, produce a promotional leaflet that could be given out at a fabric exhibition to encourage designers to use the fabric.

2 **TS** Many people think textiles are only used for clothes and furnishings. Produce a poster that makes them aware of all the other things that textile materials are used for.

Plenary

They may not always be visible, and they may not form 100 per cent of a product, but modern technical textiles are all around us.

Modern materials for protection

Objectives

In this lesson you will find out how modern fabrics are made to protect us from the environment.

Key words

membrane	an extremely thin layer of material
hydrophilic	water-loving; moisture vapour will pass through this material
laminated	fabric made from two or more different fabrics bonded together

In their search for adventure and excitement, people take part in many different activities where they need fabrics with specialized performance properties.

Protection from the weather

When Sir Robert Scott led his team of explorers to the South Pole in 1910–12 they would only have had clothes made from natural fibres. Today's explorers benefit from having a wide range of high performance textiles to keep them warm, dry and comfortable in extreme weather conditions. The technology used to develop these types of fabrics and clothing are now available for anyone taking part in winter activities or sports.

 A

Sir Robert Scott would have worn natural fibres during his expedition to the South Pole

Wind, rain and snow

Waterproof clothing used to be made from fabric (often cotton) coated with PVC. While this was good at keeping out the rain, it also made the wearer very uncomfortable because their body perspiration could not escape. Tightly-woven nylon fabric, often with a special water-resistant coating, was also widely used, but this too was not able to 'breath' and although it was light-weight it still made the wearer feel uncomfortable.

The development and use of fine **membranes** has resulted in breathable weatherproof fabrics and garments. Some membranes have millions of tiny pores in them, which allow moisture from the body to pass through them but are too small to let in liquid such as rain. Some membranes are solid, so there is no chance of the rain getting through. Moisture vapour from the body is drawn through the **hydrophilic** membrane and can escape.

The membrane can either be **laminated** onto the back of another fabric, laminated between two fabrics or used as a separate lining layer between the outer fabric and the lining fabric of a garment. There are several different manufacturers who produce membranes and fabrics with laminated membranes – you will probably recognize some of the brand names in **C**.

B *Today, Ellen MacArthur can wear high performance textiles to protect her from extreme weather conditions*

c

D *Bullet proof vests are made out of Kevlar®*

Insulation

You learned in Unit 5 that to stay warm we need to trap our body heat inside our clothes by wearing layers of clothing or garments made from fabrics with lots of air spaces in them. Some Polartec® fleece fabrics combine the insulation properties of fleece with a laminated membrane that is breathable and keeps out water.

Strong fabrics

We also need fabrics that will protect our skin from cuts and grazes if we fall or rub against hard surfaces. These fabrics may be used to make complete garments or just placed in the most vulnerable parts of clothing which cover the elbows and knees.

Cordura® is a modern fabric which is very strong but also lightweight (see **D**). It is used for rugged outerwear use, for climbing and hiking, ski and snowboarding wear, work-wear, bike-wear, gloves and backpacks.

A group of fibres called Aramid fibres have amazing strength and resistance to burning. Kevlar® is used to make bullet-proof vests and protective body wear for motor-bikers and horse riders. Nomex® is used to make special suits to protect fire fighters and racing drivers.

Think about it!

1 **TS** Carry out a test to show how trapping air in a fabric can improve its insulation properties. You could use the following fabrics and combinations of fabrics:

- polyester twill
- polyester fleece
- polyester wadding
- polyester wadding plus polyester twill.

Record your findings and comment on them.

2 **CZ** **TS** Did you know that some fleece fabrics are made from recycled plastic bottles? Find out more about one of theses fabrics by going to www.heinemann.co.uk/hotlinks and clicking on this activity.

Produce a poster to encourage consumers to demand the recycling of plastic bottles.

Plenary

The practical demands of active sports fabrics with high-performance properties have led to the development of a wide range of modern materials. These materials are now also widely used in everyday clothing.

Tough and trendy!

Objectives

In this lesson you will:

- carry out a survey to find out about backpacks
- test different fabrics to find out about performance properties and working characteristics.

Key words

compromise making decisions based on prioritising different factors

The development of new fabrics has revolutionized outdoor activities such as walking, roller-blading, biking and skateboarding with lightweight, high-performance clothing and equipment.

A

Backpacks are extremely popular for carrying all sorts of different items. Originally designed for use by people such as mountaineers and hikers, they are now used by many different people for many different functions; they can even be fashion accessories!

DMA Tough and Trendy

A bag manufacturer wants to introduce a new range of backpacks for the teenage/young adult market under the label 'Tough and Trendy'. The backpacks will need to be lightweight, weatherproof, strong and comfortable to carry leaving the hands free.

Design and make a backpack that would be suitable to include in the 'Tough and Trendy' range and could be used for a specific outdoor activity.

Think about it!

1   TS ICT ABC There are many different styles of backpacks available on the market. Carry out a survey to find out:

- which styles of backpacks are popular
- what materials they are made from
- what components have been used
- what different methods of fastenings have been used
- the types of pockets included and how useful they are
- how the backpacks are designed to be carried
- how comfortable they are to carry when full.

Record this information on a spreadsheet and analyse your results.

2   ABC Use this information to help you produce the criteria that should be included in your design specification.

The right fabric

When designing any product, it is important to make sure that the materials it is made from have the right performance properties. If you do not choose the right fabric, your backpack may look good but it will not perform well when it is used. The fabric for your

You could carry out an abrasion test

backpack needs to be strong yet lightweight and water-resistant. There are many simple tests that you could carry out in school to find out if your fabric is suitable for your backpack (**B**).

In industry, manufacturers carry out many different tests on the fabrics to make sure that they will be suitable for the products they will be made into (**C**).

Sometimes designers have to **compromise** – the fabric with the best performance properties may be expensive. This would make the product expensive and possibly unprofi

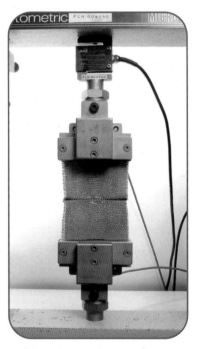

C Fabrics undergo tests to see how much they will stretch

table depending on the target market it was intended for. Designers may have to use a slightly inferior fabric because it is more affordable for the customer.

Fabrics have different working characteristics. The type of fabric will influence the processes used when manufacturing a product. This could lead to compromises in the final selection of the fabric, the design of the product or the processes used in its' manufacture.

Think about it!

1 **TS** **123** **ABC** Collect different fabrics that could be used to make your backpack.

   a) Work out how you could test the fabrics to compare their resistance to water and abrasion.

   b) Carry out the tests on the different fabrics and record your results.

   c) Produce a report to explain your findings.

   Look at **D** to see some examples of seams.

2 **TS** When you have chosen the fabrics that could be suitable for your backpack, produce different types of seams to find out:

   a) how easy or difficult it will be to produce the backpack

   b) if the seams will need to be neatened and how this could be done.

   Look at **D** to see an example of a double-stiched seam.

3 **ABC** Comment on what you have found out.

   a) How will this help you to finalize your decision about the fabric for your backpack?

   b) How has this influenced the design of your backpack?

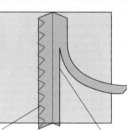

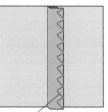

Neaten one side of the seam allowance with zig-zag

Trim one side of the seam allowance to about 6mm

Press the seam allowance to cover the trimmed side

From the right side of the fabric top stitch the seam allowance in place

D Double-stitched seam

Plenary

Choosing a suitable fabric for a product is an important part of the design process and will often involve making compromises.

Bag to basics!

Objectives

In this lesson you will:
- analyse the basic shapes used to produce different styles of backpacks
- find out about the different components that could be used in textile products.

Key words

integral   an important part of the overall design of the product

A

Backpacks usually include many features such as straps, handles, pockets and flaps. If all these were removed you would be left with a basic shape. When you go 'back to basics', backpacks that appear very different are often based on the same (or similar) basic shapes.

B

A basic shape that could be used for many different backpack designs

Think about it!

1   **PA** Analyse an existing range of backpacks and carry out a virtual disassembly on them (as described in Unit 5, pages 44–5) to identify their basic shapes.

2   **TS** Use what you have found out to decide on a basic shape that would be suitable for your backpack.

3   **ICT** Make the pattern pieces needed to produce the shape you have identified (this could be done using a pattern drafting program on the computer).

4   **FPT** Use your pattern to produce a fabric prototype to test that your pattern will work and that the backpack is a suitable size.

Customise with components

Most textile products are made from more than just fabric, they also include different components such as the thread used to stitch the product together and fastenings and trimmings that improve the function and style of the product.

It is important to think about the components you could use at the design stage; they are an **integral** part of the overall design of the product and should not just be an after-thought. Components can be categorized (grouped) as being either:
- functional: sewing thread and fastenings
- decorative: ribbons, trimmings and embroidered motifs.

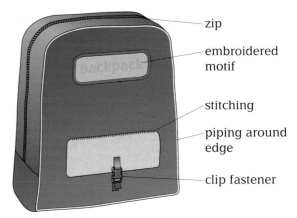

zip

embroidered motif

stitching

piping around edge

clip fastener

C   *Components can be both functional and decorative*

The components you choose will depend on:

- the type of product you are making
- where they are to be used
- the fabric the product is made from
- who will use the product
- how safe they are
- how many are needed
- how much they cost
- if they to be functional, decorative or both.

Components vary in price and will influence the final cost of a product, particularly if the product is going to be manufactured in large quantities. This is another example of how designers sometimes need to make compromises when developing products for industrial production.

Developing ideas

Once you have got the basic shape right you can begin to develop your backpack design by working out how it will be carried and how it can be made more functional or aesthetically pleasing. You will need to consider:

- using different types of fastenings and other components
- adding different style features like pockets or flaps

- using different methods for carrying
- using different types of fabric
- using more than one colour of fabric.

Think about it!

1   123 Make a list of components that could be used in your product. Carry out a survey in your local shops to find out how much each item costs.

2   TS CT Velcro® is a popular modern fastening.
   a) Find out how it was developed.
   b) Collect and mount pictures of products where Velcro® has been used to show its versatility.

3   TS Produce a design sheet showing how the basic shape you have selected for your backpack could be developed to produce a range of different designs using the ideas outlined on this page.

Plenary

Components are an important part of any textile product, so you need to find out what is available and how they could be incorporated into the design of your product. Do not just leave these decisions until you start to manufacture your product or you could have problems!

D

Design ideas

- Zip
- Clip fasteners
- Lot's of pockets
- Wide strap
- Motif

Does it work? Could it work better?

In this lesson you will:

- understand why evaluation is an important in both designing and making
- evaluate a product you have made and the way you have worked.

Key words

evaluation	thinking about why and how products are designed and made and how they function
justify	explain why you have made a decision

A This chair is being tested to see how many times it can be sat on!

Evaluation is a continuous process for manufacturers. They need to make sure that:

- their products are well designed
- the fabrics and components they use are suitable for the product
- the products are well made and will stand up to being used
- customers will buy their products or that products are improved to meet changing needs if necessary
- their production system is efficient and that their employees are fully occupied.

If manufacturers do not keep doing these things they could quickly go out of business. Evaluation leads to improvement and is the key to making or doing things better.

Think about it!

(PA) Collect examples of different types of backpacks.

1 Evaluate the backpacks to explain why they are suitable for their intended function or user. You should consider:

- the size, shape and style features
- how it is designed to be carried
- the materials and components used
- the manufacturing processes used
- the selling price.

2 Suggest what compromises the designer may have had to make such as reconciling function and aesthetics with cost.

Evaluating your own work

Evaluating existing products can help you to understand not only how products are made but also why they have been made the way they are. To make sure that the products you design meet the needs of your customer and will function well, you need to evaluate your product throughout its designing and making – not just at the end when it is finished!

Evaluating your final product

There are several aspects you need to consider when doing this:

- the design of the product
- the materials the product is made from
- the manufacture of the product.

There is only so much you can do to evaluate a product you have made yourself – you are likely to be biased! To really find out how well your product will function and if it has been successfully designed and made, you need to involve other people. You could carry out a user trial by asking someone to use the product for a while and to then make comments. Alternatively, you could so some market research amongst potential users.

As well as evaluating your product you also need to evaluate how you have worked. Look at **B**. In doing this will you be able to see how your design and technology capability is developing and set yourself targets for improvement.

Think about it!

1 **TS** **ABC** Produce a list of questions to ask as part of a market research survey about an existing backpack. You need to identify how suitable it is for its intended function or user and how it could be improved.

2 **TS** **ABC** Use the design specification you have produced for your backpack to:

   a) evaluate your different design ideas and help you decide on your final design proposal

   b) **justify** your decisions by explaining how you have satisfied each of the criteria.

3 **TS** **ABC** Carry out a user trial and market research to collect feedback about the suitability of your backpack for the target market.

   a) Determine how well the backpack functions.

   b) Decide if improvements could be made to the design/manufacture of the backpack.

   c) Use this information to produce a written report.

4 **TS** **ABC** Use the questions in **B** to write about how you worked through this assignment.

Plenary

Remember, evaluation in an on-going process. Only by reflecting on what you are doing as you work through a project, as well as when you have finished, will you produce good quality products and develop your design and technology capability.

B

How did my initial research help me to produce my design specification?

Did I finish my product?

How well did I use the tools and equipment?

How well did I use my lesson and home work time?

What problems did I have and how did I overcome them?

Did I co-operate with other people in my class?

What tools, equipment or processes do I need to practise to improve my skills?

How safely did I work?

How did I use ICT in my work, could I have made more use of this?

Who does what?

Objectives

In this lesson you will:

- find out about the different departments and their responsibilities in a modern textiles company
- learn how the computer is used to help in the production of a textile product.

Key words

lay plan	the plan of where to lay out the pattern pieces to use the least amount of fabric
job description	a description of the tasks or jobs to be completed
CIM	Computer Integrated Manufacture

In this unit you will be working on designing and manufacturing a beanie (styled soft toy) that will be batch produced.

Teamwork

'There are four people named Everybody, Somebody, Anybody and Nobody. There was an important job to be done. Everybody was asked to do it. Everybody was sure Somebody would do it.

A

Anybody could have done it, but Nobody did it. Somebody got angry about that, because it was Everybody's job. Everybody thought Anybody could do it but Nobody realized that Everybody wouldn't do it. It ended up that Everybody blamed Somebody when Nobody did what Anybody could have done.'

Textile manufacturing companies are organized into departments. Each department provides a special service to the production process, from the initial concept of the product to the production of the finished product.

The design department

This department is responsible for designing a product. This will include the production of the initial idea, the pattern and the **lay plan**.

The purchasing department

This department is responsible for finding out who can supply the fabrics and components. The fabrics and components need to be appropriately priced and of a suitable quality.

The production department

This department plans the making procedures and then organizes the manufacture of the product in the most cost effective way.

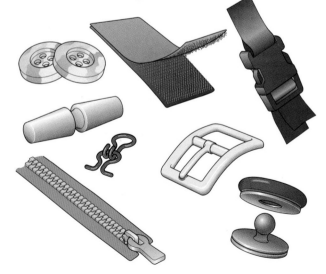

B   *There are many different components used on textile products – the purchasing department is responsible for finding out who can supply these*

The marketing department

This department is concerned with the customer and selling the required number of products at the correct price to be delivered on time.

The organizational structure of a company

A department will have a number of sections and each section has specific functions. Each department will have a manager; each section will have a supervisor; each function is carried out by an individual worker. A list of the tasks to be completed by an individual is referred to as a **job description**.

How can computers help production?

Most modern textile manufacturing companies use technology to make them more efficient. Computers are used for a number of functions within each department. CIM (computer integrated manufacturing) describes the way the computer is used for a range of different activities that take place during production. The computer is integrated into the production system in the following ways:

- computer aided administration (CAA) – computer systems are used for administration activities such as, ordering materials and costing
- computer aided design (CAD) – computer systems are used during the designing process, for example, colour ways can be changed quickly and easily on screen and with low costs. Patterns can be generated using specialized software programmes.
- production planning and control (PPC) – computer systems are used for planning the production of a product, and for monitoring the quality of the production.

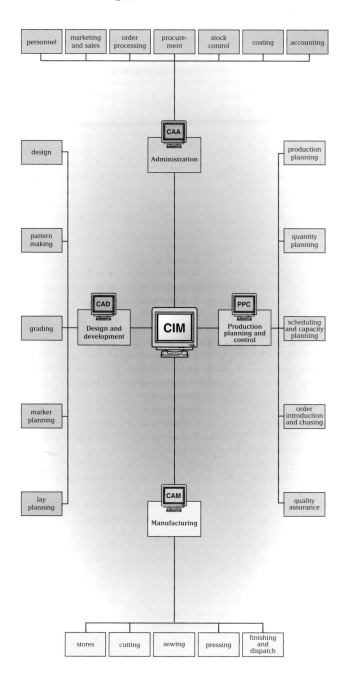

C   *CIM: computer integrated manufacture*

Think about it!

1   **ICT** Go to www.heinemann.co.uk/hotlinks to look at jobs advertised in the textile industry. Choose five jobs and for each one:

a) Write a list of the activities required for each job.

b) State which department you think the job belongs to.

2   **TS** **ICT** Take each of the following abbreviations – CIM, CAA, CAD, PPC – and illustrate what each means. Use sketches and diagrams to help you. If possible, use the Internet to find suitable pictures to illustrate these phrases.

Plenary

Manufacturing a textile product requires many different skills, from concept to mass production. Textile manufacturing involves teamwork; everyone has tasks that are dovetailed together to complete the system that manufactures the product.

Quality counts

Objectives

In this lesson you will learn how industry ensures all products are identical..

Key words

quality assurance	the system in place to ensure the quality of each product
tolerance	the amount of difference that is acceptable between two products that are said to be identical
substandard	a product that does not match the quality required
quality control	the checking that takes place throughout the manufacturing process to ensure the product is of the correct standard

How will you ensure that your beanie syled soft toys, or any product you make, will all turn out the same? We can take some tips from industry to help us with this problem.

A

Quality assurance and tolerance

As industry needs to ensure that all products are as 'identical' as possible, every manufacturing company creates a system that ensures this will happen. This means that the company can be assured that each product will be of the same quality every time it is made. The system is referred to as **quality assurance**. Any quality assurance system requires a 'master plan' or product specification (manufacturing specification) to work to. This is the base point from which everything is checked. Any acceptable variations to the product specification (manufacturing specification) are agreed at the start of production. This variation is known as the **tolerance**. Any product falling outside the tolerance will be discarded as **substandard**.

STYLE NO: MSW93
CUSTOMER & DEPT:
SEASON: A/W2001
DESCRIPTION: MENS LAMBSWOOL STRIPE ROLL NECK JUMPER
YARN & FINISH: 1 end 2/15wc 100% Woollen Spun Lambswool ex. Hinchliffe – S & S

Description / Size	M	L	XL	+	–
Front Length	72	72	75	2	1.5
Back Length					
Across Shoulders	47	49	51	2	1.5
Chest Width	59	62	65	2	1.5
Welt Width	47	50	53	2	1.5
Underarm	46	47	48	2	1.5
Armhole	27	28	29	1.5	1

B *An example of part of a manufacturing specification including tolerance levels*

Quality control

C

A quality assurance system must check that the products are being manufactured correctly and to the correct standard. **Quality control** is the checking that takes place throughout the manufacture of a product (**C**).

This checking must take place at key points in the production of the product to be sure the product will be identical every time. The product is measured or checked in some way to ensure it is within the tolerance agreed at the start of production.

It is important not to waste time and /or materials on products that will not be up to standard when complete. Waste materials have to be included in the costing of the final product and this could mean that the finished product is over priced. Specific quality control points are identified for each product produced, but general rules can be applied to any product that is to be batch or mass produced. Companies will:

- check the raw materials at the start of production
- identify a number of necessary points to be checked during the manufacture
- conduct a final check.

Every customer needs to be completely satisfied with the final product.

Think about it!

Take a beanie styled or any soft toy.
1   **PA** **TS** Sketch the toy, including the front and back view.
2   Look closely at the toy and consider how it would be manufactured.
3   Label the sketch to show where the quality control checks would be made.
4   Number the checks in the order you think they would need to be carried out.
5   Could you reduce the number of checks and still retain the quality of the final product?

Plenary

Quality control checks enforce the agreed standard for a product. Where and how these checks are made represent the quality assurance system for a product.

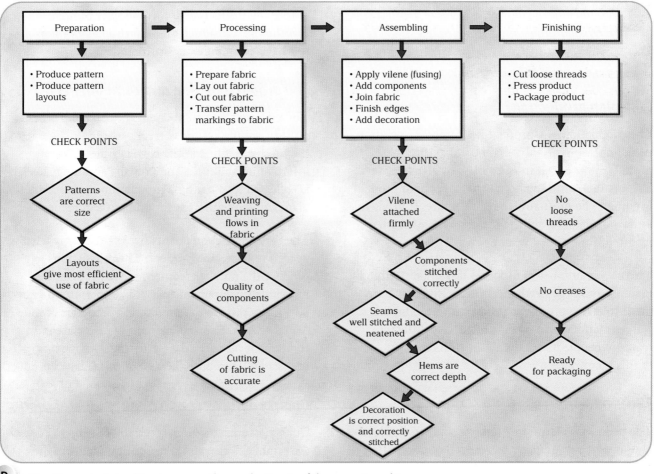

D   *Quality control checking to ensure the production is of the correct quality*

Planning for production

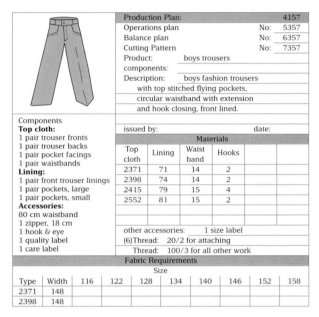

Production Plan:			4157
Operations plan		No:	5357
Balance plan		No:	6357
Cutting Pattern		No:	7357
Product:	boys trousers		
components:			
Description:	boys fashion trousers		
	with top stitched flying pockets,		
	circular waistband with extension		
	and hook closing, front lined.		

Components
Top cloth:
1 pair trouser fronts
1 pair trouser backs
1 pair pocket facings
1 pair waistbands
Lining:
1 pair front trouser linings
1 pair pockets, large
1 pair pockets, small
Accessories:
80 cm waistband
1 zipper, 18 cm
1 hook & eye
1 quality label
1 care label

issued by:			date:	
Materials				
Top cloth	Lining	Waist band	Hooks	
2371	71	14	2	
2398	74	14	2	
2415	79	15	4	
2552	81	15	2	
other accessories:	1 size label			
(6)Thread:	20/2 for attaching			
Thread:	100/3 for all other work			

Fabric Requirements									
		Size							
Type	Width	116	122	128	134	140	146	152	158
2371	148								
2398	148								

A An example of a production plan, including an individual components list

marketing team. This information is brought together on a **production plan** that may or may not have a components list included.

The production plan and components list

The materials and components to make the product must be sourced at the correct price and delivered to the production line at the correct time. The information about the components and the materials is collected together on a production plan. Production plans can look different in different companies.

The individual components list states exactly what is needed to make one product. The calculations to produce the number required are made from the individuals components list. It is important to know how many products are required at the start of the planning, so the correct amount of materials and components are priced. Purchasing components in bulk can often reduce the cost of the finished product.

Why plan production?

The production of a product is a complex operation, which must be carefully planned to ensure the product is produced in the most cost effective way. The manufacturer must know that a certain product is going to be profitable to manufacture. It needs to know how many products it can produce, in what length of time and at what price.

There are a number of different tasks that need to be planned and organized once the decision has been made to take a prototype product into production. Larger manufacturing companies have different teams of people dealing with the different elements of this planning.

The production team

The production team in a large textile manufacturing company has the job of dovetailing all the different tasks, to ensure the product is completed to time to fulfil the orders taken by the

Quality assurance and quality control checks

Quality assurance systems need to be set up to ensure the product is checked at the critical points in the course of the production. These controls checks are different for each product and need to be carefully

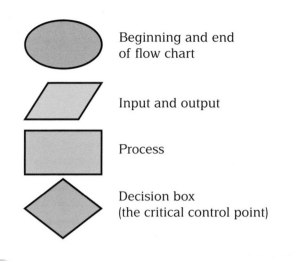

Operations Plan: 5357		

Production Plan No. 4157
Balance Plan No. 6357
Product: boys trousers
Total time: 18.50 minutes

No.	Operation	Equipment	Time min
1	1 pair trouser fronts, attach lining	O/L	2.15
2	1 pair trouser backs, attach	O/L	1.75
3	1 pair pockets, attach facings	L/S	0.35
4	1 pair pockets, seem all round	O/L	0.40

B *An example of an operations plan*

D *BSI flow chart symbols*

Beginning and end
of flow chart

Input and output

Process

Decision box
(the critical control point)

organized. See pages 72–3 for more detailed information about quality assurance and quality control.

Operations plan (manufacturing specification)

The quickest and most effective processes and techniques of making the product are planned out and are recorded in the operations plan (see **B**).

Pressing and packaging

After the product has been finally checked it is then pressed (**C**) and suitably packaged to protect it from dirt and damage on its journey to the market place.

Scheduling the manufacturing of your own products using flow charts and gantt charts

Flow charts

Production flow charts are systems that can be used to organize the way a product is manufactured. The

British Standard Insitute (BSI) 4058 have a set of symbols for flow charts which can be used to instruct the manufacture of a prototype.

These symbols help you to think and organize exactly what needs to be completed in what order. They make sure that you include the checking points to ensure your product is of the correct quality. They also allocate the time required to complete each element of the production of the product. An arrow is used to show the direction of the flow.

A gantt chart

A **gantt chart** is another way of planning the production of a textile product. It plans out the time allotted to each process to ensure the product is completed to deadline.

In any production plan there is a need to plan time for unforeseen circumstances such as the breakdown of vital equipment, power cuts, the supplier not getting the materials to the factory at the correct time, and so on.

Think about it!

Using the BSI flow chart symbols, produce a flow chart to show how to make a cup of tea.

Plenary

Planning the production of a product is important to the successful manufacture of the product.

C

How much will it cost?

Objectives

In this lesson you will learn how industry prices a product.

Costing a product

Costing a textile product is a very complex task. It has to be costed accurately, otherwise it may not be profitable to batch or mass manufacture the designed product. Costing includes charging for every aspect of the production of a product, from the market research to advertising the product to the customer.

The following activities and items need to be priced:
- market research to find a gap in the market
- designing the product to match the findings from the market research
- pattern drafting
- planning the pattern layout economically (waste materials need to be included in the cost)
- producing sample products/prototypes
- electricity needed to operate the equipment and to provide heating and lighting in the manufacturing unit
- materials needed to make the product: the fabric, components and thread
- quality control checks: faulty products and components must be charged for

- equipment: either the cost of purchasing or the cost of hiring equipment both large and small
- time: the labour charges or wages of the workers that are employed
- safety equipment that is need by the production workers to make the product
- packaging costs: both simple and elaborate packaging ranging from simple plastic bags, complex printed cartons or nets used.

The above activities and items can be divided under two headings: fixed costs and variable costs.

Fixed costs are the costs that will be present regardless of the number of products produced. Examples of fixed costs include electricity, rent for the manufacturing unit, insurance for the employees and the cost of purchasing or hiring and servicing machinery.

The variable costs will vary depending on the number of products produced. Examples of variable costs include materials needed to manufacture the products and wages for employees.

Working out the costs of a product

The above list may have presented you with some surprises. Would you have thought of all of these items? Once you have figures or estimated figures for all these activities, you are then in a position to calculate the cost (see **B**).

A

Spreadsheet 1

Fixed costs	Costs per week £
Rent	60
Telephone	5
Loan repayments	20
Equipment maintenance	10
Lighting and heating	5
Wages	300
TOTAL	**£400**

Spreadsheet 2

Variable costs	Cost per jumper £				
Materials	5.75				
Power	0.25				
TOTAL	**£6.00**				
Number of jumpers made	0	20	40	60	80	100
Fixed costs	£400	£400	£400	£400	£400	£400
Variable costs	£0	£120	£240	£360	£480	£600
TOTAL	**£400**	**£520**	**£640**	**£760**	**£880**	**£1000**

B

Think about it!

ICT 123 Set up two spreadsheets to help you calculate the cost of manufacturing one Beanie Buddy and one hundred Beanie Buddies.

Hint: Use one spreadsheet for fixed costs and another for variable costs. You will need to add the two spreadsheets together to get the actual cost.

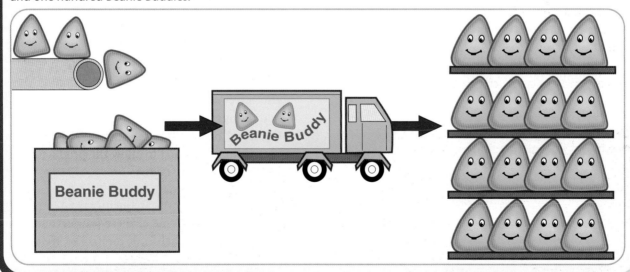

Plenary

Costing the production of a product is important to the success of the product. The costing of a product must be completed accurately, so the company producing the product doesn't go bankrupt. Everything used to make the product must be priced or accounted for when costing a product.

Marketing–buy one, get one free!

What is marketing?

Marketing is about satisfying people's needs at the correct price. It is about finding out what people want, producing what they want at the correct price and then promoting and selling the products in a suitable place.

Marketing includes four main areas:
- advertising
- packaging
- display
- research.

Market research

Many new products are produced each year; some are very successful, others are not. Market research can help to minimise the risks when launching a new product. Market research tries to find out the answers to questions that the manufacturer needs to know either by desk research or by field research. Desk research uses information that has already been produced by other resources. Field research involves market researchers finding out the information themselves through questionnaires and surveys. Market researchers target the client or customer that the product is aimed at and asks them some relevant questions. The results are then analyzed and provide the manufacturing company with the information they require.

Advertising

Advertising involves the manufacturers communicating with the client/customer. To advertize the product, the manufacturers inform, explain and persuade:
- inform: they give the customer information about the product
- explain: they tell the customer what the product can do
- persuade: the customer is enticed to buy the product.

Advertising can be done through television, radio, magazines, newspaper, posters and adverts on the side of buses, in underground stations and on roadside hoardings.

Packaging

Most textile products do not require specialized packaging. Many textile products are packaged when they are bought and are ready to be taken out of the shop. They are placed into a plastic carrier bag, which usually has the retailing company's logo on the side.

When a product such as a shirt is packaged, the packaging serves three purposes:
- protection: packaging protects textile products from damage and staining during storage and transportation
- information: bar codes on packaging help companies automatically keep control of their stock; packaging also gives information on the after care of the product
- marketing: packaging helps the product to be displayed effectively – a header card with a plastic hook attached to allow the product to be hung on a display stand.

Card plastic and paper are frequently used to package the textile products. Some of these products are biodegradable. Manufacturing companies are under pressure to consider the impact on the environment when designing and producing packaging.

What information must be on the packaging of a textile product?

The following information is frequently included in the packaging (**A**).

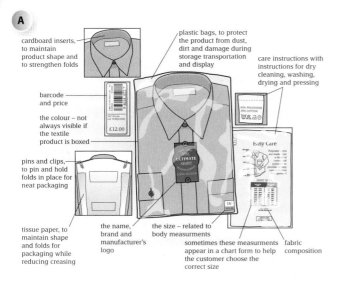

A

cardboard inserts, to maintain product shape and to strengthen folds

plastic bags, to protect the product from dust, dirt and damage during storage transportation and display

care instructions with instructions for dry cleaning, washing, drying and pressing

barcode and price

the colour – not always visible if the textile product is boxed

pins and clips, to pin and hold folds in place for neat packaging

tissue paper, to maintain shape and folds for packaging while reducing creasing

the name, brand and manufacturer's logo

the size – related to body measurments

sometimes these measurments appear in a chart form to help the customer choose the correct size

fabric composition

Display

The way products are displayed will greatly affect the sales of that product. Shops spend money on displaying their products to encourage the customer to buy them. Large companies usually have a window display which encourages customers to go into the shop (see **B**). Once customers are inside the shop, the retailer looks at producing point of sale displays to encourage them to buy the products (**C**).

Clothing is usually displayed on mannequins in high street stores, or they may be displayed at a fashion show where live models wear the clothes. This is usually the way haute couture fashion houses sell their clothes. Some companies do not have high street stores but sell their products through catalogues in which photographs are used to sell the products.

B

C

Think about it!

Take an existing beanie styled or soft toy or the beanie toy you have made.

Design an information leaflet to accompany the toy when it is sold. Your information leaflet must include the following information about the toy:

- a sketch
- the name
- the price
- a care label for the toy
- a letter to the customer about the good points of the toy
- quotes from customers who have purchased the toy
- the name and address of the manufacturer
- any other information you feel would be good for the customer to know.

Plenary

Marketing is as important as the designing and making of the product. Without a successful marketing department, the manufactured product may not be sold to the customer, which ultimately means that no profit is made and the company goes bankrupt.

The target customer

Customers select products for very different reasons. This can be regardless of their age or whether they are male or female. Customers can be grouped in the following categories.

- *Fashion worshippers or style leaders:* people who are prepared to pay lots of money for exclusive items.
- *Style followers:* people who will purchase products once they are more readily available and at a reduced price.
- *Average consumers:* people who purchase the product once the style is not so extreme and has been simplified and sold at a more reasonable price.
- *Decline laggards:* people who purchase the products once the majority of people have moved on to another style and so they get the product at bargain prices. These people are not worried about style and are more concerned about the price of the products.

The groups of people listed above reflect the **product cycle** (see **A**). The product cycle helps designers and manufacturers to know when to introduce new products. The sales of a product are watched carefully and once a product reaches peak sales then new products are required to replace that product.

Customer profiles

Customer profiles help designers and manufactures to produce products for customers of specific companies. The customer profile will guide a designer to produce a product that is suitable for the customer.

Outlet:	Top Shop
	Female
Age:	15–24
Income:	£7–10,000 per annum
Magazines:	More; Sugar; J-17
Shops:	Clothing – Top Shop; Miss Selfridge; New Look
	Cosmetics – SuperDrug
Music:	Blue; Sugababes; Ministry of Sound
TV:	Friends; Ally McBeal; TOTP; Dawson's Creek; South Park
Pursuits:	Cinema; Clubbing; Live concerts
Idols:	Male – Leonardo di Caprio; Michael Owen
	Female – Jennifer Aniston; Janet Jackson
Eating out:	MacDonalds

B   *An example of a customer profile*

A
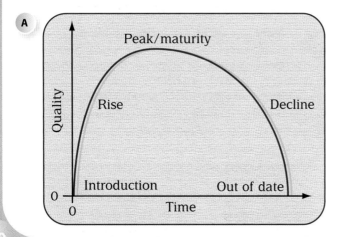

People and products

When you look at any product carefully you can begin to predict who might wish to own that product or who might purchase it. You look for clues to help you make these predictions as accurate as possible. You look at the style, the line, shape and form, the image, the kind of fabrics, patterns and colours used to manufacture the product. All of these clues help us to make these predictions.

This type of exercise is very helpful to a designer when designing new products. The art of successful designing is to be able to step into the shoes of the target customer and predict what they will like or dislike. This is an excellent skill to have.

Think about it!

1   TS Look at the customer profile in **B**.

   a) Create a customer profile for a 14–16 year old teenager for a high street store of your choice.

   b) Use table **C** to help you present the information.

C

Outlet	
Gender and age	**Male/female, 14–16 years old**
Magazines	
Shops	
Music	
TV	
Pursuits	
Idols	
Eating out	

2   ABC Match the customers in **D** with a suitable mobile phone case shown in **E**. Write a report to say why you have selected the specific phone case for each target customer.

D

Plenary

Products are designed for specific customers to portray specific images. A designer needs to work alongside the information about the target customer to ensure the product is what the target customer will like.

E

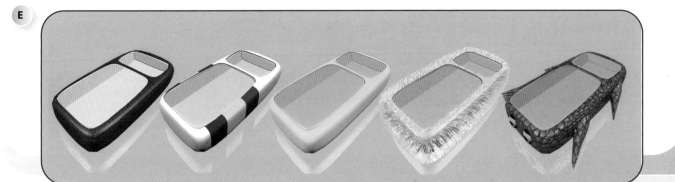

Computer aided design

Objectives

In this lesson you will:

- find out how CAD is used in the design of textile products in industry
- use CAD in the classroom to assist in the design of your own textile products.

Key words

graphics programs software programs that enable you to draw and add colour

rapid prototyping using CAD to produce prototype products

Computer technology has revolutionized the way textile products are designed and made in industry. Many of these processes can also be carried out in a similar way in the classroom.

Designing fabrics

Producing a length of woven or printed fabric involves setting up complicated machinery, which is time consuming and would be costly to change if the design of the fabric needed to be altered.

Using CAD to design new fabrics enables the designer to try out a variety of different ideas and make necessary alterations so that the design is exactly right before the machines are set up.

Designing textile products

Designers need to show their clients what their products would look like in order for them to be approved. By using CAD, the designer can quickly develop design sheets which show how the product would look in different types of fabric or in different colourways. In school you could use Speed Step software or other **graphics programs** in a similar way.

Fabric that has been designed on the computer can be printed onto treated fabric using special inks. In industry, short lengths of digitally printed fabric can be used to produce prototype garments so that a client can see what the product will look like made up in fabric before the order for the fabric and product is finalized. This is called **rapid prototyping**.

Drafting patterns

CAD can be used to design and store basic pattern pieces which can then be retrieved and easily modified to meet changing fashions.

Garment patterns need to be produced in a range of different sizes. The pattern technician will draft a pattern in one size and then, at the touch of a button, the computer will work out the pattern pieces in a range of other sizes. This process is called grading.

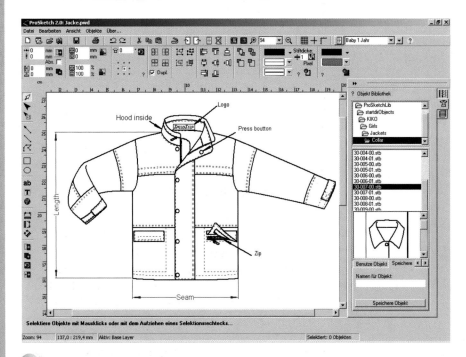

A *Pro-Sketch Software can be used to design products*

B

Producing lay plans

In industry many single layers of fabric are spread out on top of each other on a cutting table. Planning the best way to place the pattern pieces onto the fabric is very important. Using a computer program

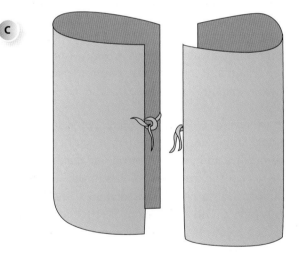

C

Front   Back

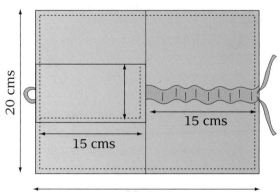

20 cms

15 cms

15 cms

30 cms

makes this process quicker and more accurate. The operator can move the pattern pieces around on the screen to get the best arrangement.

There are several different pattern-drafting software programs that are available for use in school, such as Pattern Maker (Pro-Specs) and Fittingly Sew (Soft Byte). In addition to being used for drafting patterns for garments, these can also be used to draft the patterns for other textile products. They will also enable you to calculate how much fabric is required to make one or more products and to work out lay plans.

Think about it!

1   (CT) a) Produce a black and white line drawing of your product (use a fine-line pen for a good result).

   b) Scan your design into a graphics program.

   c) Copy your line design about five or six times.

   d) Use the fill tools in the program to colour each copy in a different colourway.

   e) Copy and paste your coloured designs into a word document.

   f) Re-size the different images and arrange them on the document.

   g) Add a title and annotation to your design sheet using one or more of the following:

   ● text

   ● callouts

   ● WordArt.

2   (CT) a) Use a pattern-drafting program to develop the pattern pieces you need for your product.

   (123) b) Fabric is available in different widths: 90cm, 115cm and 150cm. Work out a suitable lay plan to cut out twenty identical products from each of these widths of fabric.

Plenary

Using computers during the design process enables manufacturers to develop design ideas and prototype products in a fraction of the time it would have taken using traditional methods. Find out about the CAD facilities you have in school and try to make use of them as much as possible when designing your own textile products.

Computer aided manufacture

Objectives

In this lesson you will:
- find out how CAM is used in industry and school
- understand that CAD and CAM are often used together.

Using computers to control machines during the making process ensures consistency and quality in the manufacture of identical parts or complete products. Industrial sewing machines are designed to perform specific functions or carry out specific processes in the manufacture of textile products. Many of these can be computer-controlled so that each time the process is carried out it is identical.

In school you could use a computerized sewing machine to produce buttonholes. Usually a special presser foot is needed for this process. Once the size and style of buttonhole have been set the machine will produce any number of identical buttonholes (**B**).

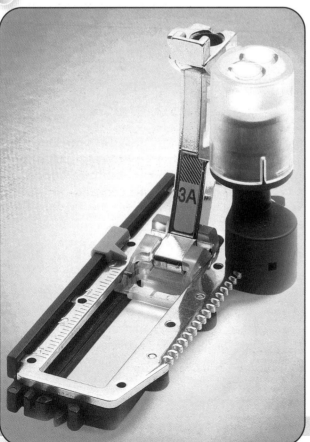

A

Very often CAD and CAM are used together. A designer can develop a design using CAD software, which is then programmed into the CAM software of the manufacturing machine. The entire process from design to manufacture is known as the CAD/CAM process.

Cutting out fabric

In large companies computer controlled laser cutters can be used to cut out the different fabric shapes. The lay plan, produced by a pattern technologist using CAD, is programmed into the CAM software in the cutting machine which controls the laser cutter.

CNC embroidery

Embroidered designs and logos are used on a wide variety of industrially-produced textile products. This is a good example of how CAD and CAM work together. The embroidery design is developed on the computer using a CAD program and the digitized information is transferred to the CAM program in the embroidery machine. The CAD/CAM principles used to design and manufacture embroidered logos in industry are similar to those in school.

There are several types of industrial embroidery machines. Single head embroidery machines have several needles and presser feet on one machine. This is so that the different colours in the embroidery design can be threaded up at the start of the embroidery. Only one colour is stitched at a time, but as each colour is needed the appropriate needle and presser foot are used automatically. This saves

Think about it!

1. **TS** Find out how buttonholes are produced on the sewing machine you use in school.
2. Produce samples of the different types of buttonhole the machine will produce.
3. Produce a flow chart showing the programmed stages in sewing a buttonhole.
4. **D** Produce some alternative design ideas for your product to show how buttons and buttonholes could be used as a fastening.

B *Embroidered designs and logos are used on many industrially produced products*

the operator from having to stop and re-thread the machine for each colour in the design.

Multi-head machines are several embroidery machines linked together and controlled by a single computer. This means that the same design can be sewn onto several different products at the same time.

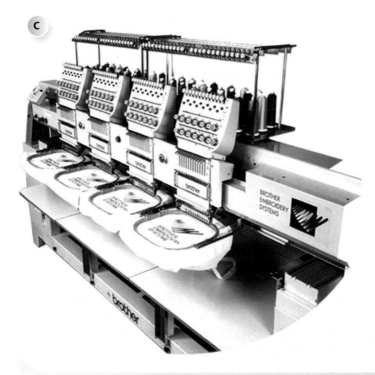

Flat-bed embroidery machines are used to embroider designs onto flat pieces of fabric. This means the garment pieces are embroidered whilst they are still flat, before they are assembled with the other garment pieces.

Drop head embroidery machines are used to stitch embroidery designs onto garments that have already been constructed – for example, baseball hats.

Another situation where CAD and CAM work together is when using the CAMM 1 machine. Designs produced in the CAD drawing software are cut out in plastic or card using CAM.

Think about it!

1 **ICT** Use a CAD program to develop a simple logo that could be included on the front of your product.

2 **ICT** Produce the design using CAM.

Plenary

Many of the CAD/CAM processes you use in school for producing one-off products or small quantities of identical products are the same as those used in industry to produce large volumes of products.

Planning production

Objectives

In this lesson you will learn how to plan the manufacture of a product in volume using the progressive bundle system.

Key words

progressive bundle system   bundles of pieces needed to make a product are passed along a production line

When a textile product is to be manufactured in quantity it is important to use the correct system to ensure the product is made in the most effective and efficient way. One of the most frequently used systems is referred to as the **progressive bundle system** (see Unit 5, page 52). This is one method industry uses to produce products in volume.

Before a product goes into volume production, the tasks that must be completed to make the product are identified. The tasks are grouped together into a 'section of the production'. The factory manager then organizes the correct number of machinist needed for each section of the production. Each machinist completes one specific job in the production line. Once one section of the product has been completed, the partly finished product is bundled up again and then passed to the next set of machinists to complete the next step in the manufacturing of the product. This process is difficult to imagine, but if we look at a real example if should become clearer. Look at the product in A and the fabric pieces in B.

A

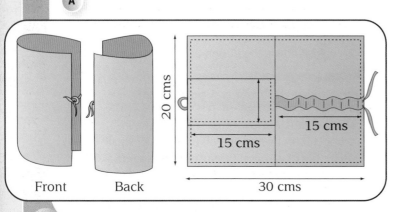

Front   Back   30 cms

20 cms   15 cms   15 cms

B

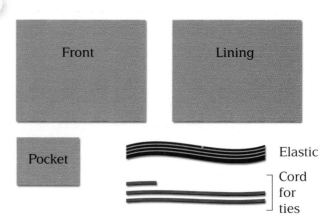

Front   Lining   Pocket   Elastic   Cord for ties

List all the jobs that must be completed to make the product. At this stage it is not important to have them in the correct order.

- The CAM motif needs to be stitched onto the front of the container.
- The pocket needs to be made.
- The pocket needs to be attached to the lining.
- The elastic needs to be stitched in place on the lining.
- The hoop needs to be attached to the front of the container.
- The ties need to be attached to the back portion of the container.
- The outer section of the container needs to be attached to the lining RS together and stitched around trapping the hoop and ties in place.
- The container needs to be turned through to the RS.
- The edge of the container needs to be top stitched to hold the lining in place and the hole used to turn the product through needs to be stitched up.
- The container needs to be folded in half and pressed to finish it.

The next step is to plan out what is the quickest and most effective order to complete these tasks. The choice of the processes and the order of the processes to make the container will make a difference as to how long it will take to make the product. A small saving in time when multiplied for many products will affect the labour cost and consequently the cost of manufacture. It is important that this system is planned accurately and carefully.

The tasks are then grouped into sections. The list below shows how it might work for the container.

1. Making and attaching the pocket to the lining.

2. Stitching the CAM motif in the correct position on the outer section.

3. Positioning the hoop and the ties in the correct position on the front of the container.

4. Stitching the elastic to the lining.

5. Joining the outer section and lining together.

6. Turning through and top stitching.

7. Pressing the final product to ensure a good finish.

Each section then needs to be organized in the correct position on the production line to ensure little time is wasted transferring each bundle to the next section of machinists.

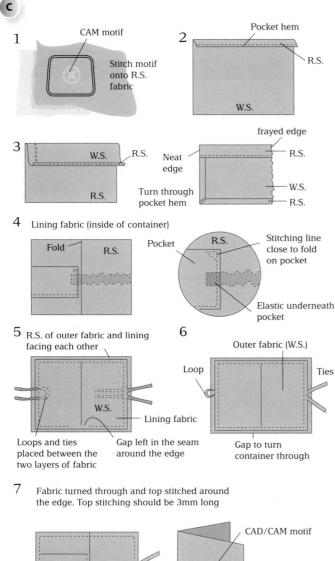

A, B, C machinist completing a part of the product
D, E: bundles of fabric pieces ready to be stitched together

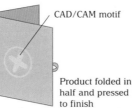

Think about it!

1 **TS** How many different ways can you think of to organize the sections of work to make this simple container?

2 **TS** Which would be the most efficient one and why?

3 **TS** What are the advantages of the progressive bundling system in making the container?

Plenary

Planning the production of a product needs great care and attention to the detail to make sure the product is produced in the most cost effective way possible. The first step is to think about the activities needed to make the product and then to plan the most efficient order for the activities to take place.

Health and safety in the workplace

Objectives

In this lesson you will:

- find out how industry ensures the workplace is as safe as possible
- learn how to work in a safe manner.

Both the making of fabrics and the manufacturing of products from fabrics can be dangerous procedures. Dyes and finishes applied to fabrics use hazardous chemicals. Textile manufacturing units use tools and machines that are designed to cut, pierce and press fabrics. Even though the textile industry is potentially hazardous, it is important to ensure the workplace is as safe as possible.

The Health and Safety at Work Act 1974 was drawn up to protect employees from hazards at work. The Act requires employers to:

- provide safety training
- maintain machines
- provide a set of rules to work safely (a safety policy)
- provide first aid facilities
- provide health premises.

This Act was also designed to raise the awareness of employees to the hazards that occur in the workplace. Raising the awareness of the possible dangers when using a machine or when carrying out a process can help people to work with more care and attention; this in itself can reduce the number of accidents. Frequently accidents are a result of a lapse in concentration or from people taking an additional risk. Being careful and safe is about being aware. To ensure the employee is as safe as possible in the workplace a risk assessment is carried out to establish what risks are involved in completing a procedure or a process.

Once the possible accidents or hazards are identified then action is taken to reduced the risk to a minimum. This involves:

- a set of rules to inform people how to operate a machine
- instructions about what specific protective clothing must be worn whilst working with chemicals used to dye and finish fabrics.

Sometimes the employee can find the safety procedures irritating, as they can make the task longer or the protective clothing feels uncomfortable. Employees must understand, however, that safety rules are in place to protect them.

Think about it!

You have been asked to carry out a health and safety audit or risk assessment in your school's textiles workshop.

1 **TS** Identify five risks to people's health in your textile workshop.
2 **ABC** For each risk, write a report outlining what the threat to people's health might be.
3 Prepare a set of safety rules for three of these risks.
4 Produce a poster for one risk that could be used to inform the user of the safe way to use the machine.

Plenary

Even though the textile industry can be hazardous, it is important to ensure the workplace is as safe as possible. This is done by considering the possible accidents in the manufacturing unit and then reducing these risks as much as possible, by using a variety of strategies with the employees such as rules of conduct, appropriate signs, and training.

A

Cutting hand with equipment

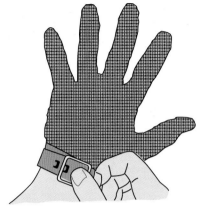

Wearing chainmail gloves

Stitching finger

Keeping fingers well away
from the needle
Going slowly over difficult tasks

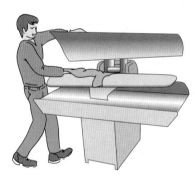

Burning fingers, hand, face

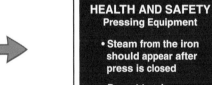

HEALTH AND SAFETY
Pressing Equipment

- Steam from the iron
  should appear after
  press is closed

- Do not touch
  the hot plates

Following guidelines on safe
use of equipment

Tripping or falling over waste
material

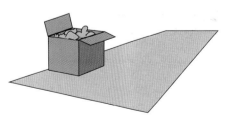

Keeping work area clean and tidy

Needs and wants

We all develop as we pass through the various phases of life from babyhood, through childhood, adolescence, adulthood and old age.

A

During each phase of life our needs and wants vary. As we grow we are more capable of understanding the world around us and our desires change. Designers need to consider the needs and wants of the client or customer when designing products to solve particular problems.

People's needs and wants can be grouped in the following ways.

- *Physical needs*: we all need food, water, and air to breath; we need to be kept warm and be protected from the weather; we need to exercise frequently to keep our body functioning well.
- *Intellectual needs*: we all need to exercise our brains; we need to learn new things; we need to be excited and motivated to use our brains.
- *Emotional needs*: we all need to feel safe and secure; we need to feel wanted and cared for; we need to have ways to express our emotional feelings.
- *Social needs*: we like to spend time with friends and doing things together this is a social need.

The basic needs of a person, such as food and friendship, remain constant regardless of the stage of development. But the way the needs are met must match the likes and dislikes of the person. For example, the clothes of an elderly person must meet a very different set of needs than the clothes of a young adult. These needs must be considered when designing for a client or customer.

Professional designers and how they work

When a professional designer is presented with a design situation, he or she will buy magazines that are targeted at the customer they are designing for. By looking through the magazines it helps the designer to step into the shoes of the potential clients: the colours, the style of presentation, the language used, the size of print, the layout of the magazine all hint at what appeals to the customer.

B

This helps the designer to design with a real knowledge and understanding of the client. This must happen to ensure time is not wasted designing products that are totally unsuitable.

C

Think about it!

1 Produce an image board that helps you to understand an older person's likes and dislikes.

2 Produce a report on the findings from your research about the older person.

3 CZ In a small group, or as a class, produce a wall display entitled 'The older person'. Use the image boards and the reports produced by the group to help inform other students about older people.

A

Plenary

Throughout our lives our physical, intellectual, emotional and social needs develop and change. When designing products, designers must consider the target customers' needs and wants, which are governed by their physical, intellectual, emotional and social needs.

Getting ready for Key Stage 4

During Key Stage 3 you have been developing your skills in designing, making and evaluating (justifying and reviewing). You have also been developing your skills in communicating. You have a good idea of the activities you prefer to work on, the ones that you learned the most from. You will know what your strengths and weaknesses are.

What you have to do now is to reflect on your own performance, consider how you have progressed, record what you know and set yourself some real targets to work towards. By thinking hard and recording honestly, you will be able to see where you need to focus your efforts over the next two years.

Targets – taking control of your attainment

Setting yourself a target is the first step to improve your attainment. Once you have established what you find difficult, you can start to consider what you need to do to get better.

Think about it!

1 Draw a table similar to table **A**.

a) Think about your own performance (your subject knowledge, designing skills, making skills, and your ability to evaluate and communicate) and complete the table.

b) Look closely at exactly what you can do and make a list of these things.

c) Look at where you are not performing as well. Make a list of these areas too.

d) Set yourself targets to improve these areas and state how you intend to do this.

2 From the table you have completed on your performance, identify a maximum of five areas you need to work on.

a) For each area, identify what exactly you are going to do to get better at the skill.

b) Draw yourself a table similar to **B** and record your targets. Remember that you need to state how you intend to achieve them.

Plenary

To reflect on your own strengths and weaknesses and to set yourself targets based on this information is a good way to improve your attainment levels.

Area for development	Can do	Can do well	Need to improve
The design process			
Designing skills			
Clarifying the task			
Understanding the task			
Interpreting the task			
Recording the design considerations			
Generating ideas			
Evolving ideas, adapting and adjusting ideas			
Diversifying ideas, wide range of possible ideas			
Proposing design possibilities			
Developing ideas			
Modelling design possibilities			

A Achievements at the end of Key Stage 3

Refining design ideas			
Stating how the product could be made techniques and processes to be used			
Communicating intentions			
Verbally			
Graphically-technical, visual and pictorial			
Modelling			
Producing quality products			
Planning			
Materials needed			
Equipment required			
Making sequence time plan			
Working with materials			
Selecting, measuring, marking out			
Cutting, shaping, joining fabrics			
Health and safety issues			
Using tools and equipment safely			
Recognizing hazards			
Evaluating skills – justifying and reviewing processes and products			
During designing and making			
After designing and making			
Learning methods – the way you learn best			
Focused practical tasks – being taught skills through demonstration and practice			
Design skills			
Making skills			
Product analysis			
Looking at existing products			
Design and make assignments			
Independent work			
Team work			

Skills area to improve	How to improve it
To record my design ideas quickly	Giving myself a time scale to work to Practising sketching ideas quickly
To improve the quality of finish of my products	Be more accurate while making my products

B *Setting targets*

Glossary

Absorbency the ability to soak up moisture

Appliqué the decorative process of attaching one fabric to another using stitches

Average consumers customers who purchase a product once it has been simplified and is at a reasonable price

Balance wheel, take-up lever, presser foot, feed-dog different parts of the sewing machine

Bobbin a spool onto which thread is wound

Breathable fabrics fabrics that move perspiration away from our bodies and through our clothing

CAD Computer aided design

CAM Computer aided manufacture

CIM Computer integrated manufacture

CNC Computer numerical control

Characteristics the qualities of a fibre

Components additional pieces that are added to a product

Compromise making decisions based on prioritising different factors

Continuous filament fibre a very long fibre

'Cool peel' transfer paper a special paper which is fed through a colour printer

Craft production individually designed and manufactured products

Criteria rules or points against which something is judged or checked

Customer profile common factors of customers in the target market

Cutting line the edge of the pattern, shows where to cut out the fabric

Disassembly taking a product apart to see how it has been constructed

Drape how a fabric hangs

Dye a liquid form of colour

Dye bath the container and the dye

Equipment the tools used to make the materials into products

Evaluation thinking about why and how products are designed and made and how they function

Evaporation when liquid turns into vapour

Facing a separate piece of fabric used to finish the edge of part of a product

Fibre the smallest part of a fabric

Fixative the chemicals that react with the dye to ensure the colour is permanently held in the fabric

Fluorescent fabric a brightly coloured fabric that reflects light rays

Fraying where the yarn comes away from the cut edge easily

Functional or utility stitches stitches that are used to construct products

Gantt chart a chart that maps out the activities which take place in order to produce a product

Grain line shows how to line up the pattern with the yarns in the fabric

Graphics programs software programs that enable you to draw and add colour

Handle what the fabric is like to hold and work with

Hem a way of finishing the edge of a piece of fabric

Hydrophilic water-loving. Moisture vapour will pass through this material

Image board a visual representation of the customer/target market

Industrial production large quantities of identical products produced for a target customer

Integral an important part of the overall design of the product

Job description a description of tasks or jobs to be completed

Justify explain why you have made a decision

Laminated fabric made from two or more different fabrics bonded together

Lay plan the plan of where to lay out the pattern pieces to use the least amount of fabric

Lockstitch sewing machine stitch formed using two different threads

Logo a symbol that represents a company or organization

Materials the different items products are made from

Membrane an extremely thin layer of material

Micro-fibre very fine fibre

Motif an image; unit of pattern

Notches show on a pattern where two different fabric pieces need to match together

Organza a very fine, strong, transparent fabric

Overlocker a special kind of sewing machine that forms a chain stitch

Pattern a paper shape used as a template for cutting out fabric pieces; a sequence of recurring shapes

Pattern drafting the process of making patterns for textile products

Pattern markings special symbols marked onto pattern pieces to help you make the product accurately

Performance the way a fabric behaves

Pile raised surface on a fabric

Printing ink a thick (viscose) dye

Printing pad a spongy pad coated in printing ink used to apply ink to the block

Prioritize decide what is most and/or least important

Product cycle the pattern of people purchasing a product

Production flow chart a flow chart that clearly outlines what needs to be completed what order

Production plan (product specification) a description of the product and a list of materials and components required to make the product

Production system the organization of manufacturing products

Progressive bundle system bundles of pieces needed to make a product are passed along a production line

Quality assurance the system in place to ensure the quality of each product

Quality control the checking that takes place throughout the manufacturing process to ensure the product is of the correct standard

Rapid prototyping using CAD to produce prototype products

Reflective fabric light is reflected from the surface of the fabric

Resist technique of dying where the dye is prevented from entering some parts of a fabric

Scale of production the quantity of products to be manufactured

Screen a frame that has fabric stretched across it

Seam a join to hold two or more pieces of fabric together

Seam allowance the distance between the cutting line and the stitching line

Shrinkage how much a fabric has been reduced in size once it has been wet

Smart textiles materials that are able to react to the user or the environment

Squeegee a tool that pushes the ink through the screen

Staple fibre a short fibre

Stitching line the line that shows where to sew. Also called the seam line

Stitching template a template that identifies exactly where the stitching is to be placed

Substandard a product that does not match the quality required

Target customer the person or group of people a product is designed for

Target market the group of customers that a product is designed for

Technical textiles fibres or fabrics developed for their special performance properties

Toile mock-up made from fabric of a garment such as a hat

Tolerance the amount of difference that is acceptable between two products that are said to be identical

Virtual disassembly imagining a product if it was taken apart

Wicking the process of transporting moisture along a fabric

Working characteristics how a fabric behaves when it is being manufactured into products

Yarn group of fibres twisted together

Index